MW00848584

# Praise for
## *The Gentle Traditionalist*

This is one of the most unusual books I've ever read. It's a spiritual journey, a romance and a quest; a reflection on history and a discourse on faith and tradition; a fable and a meditation about place and location. It's sometimes surreal, sometimes eccentric, sometimes didactic, but written throughout with passion and engagement, with a touching and deep-seated love for Ireland and for the sweetness and humanity that have been embedded in Irish country values. Some readers will want to argue with the text. Others will be stimulated to ponder the question whether in the course of modernisation, globalised Ireland has lost the essence that was its soul.—MARY KENNY, author of *Goodbye to Catholic Ireland* and *Crown and Shamrock*

The Socratic Dialogue is a literary form quite literally as old as Western Civilisation. Boethius, Joseph de Maistre, and Vladimir Solovyov— among countless others—made use of it to critique the societies and world-views under which they lived. Now Roger Buck in *The Gentle Traditionalist* employs this age-old genre to examine that which would prefer not to be examined—the Western secular "religion" that has come to define the society under which we in the so-called "developed" world all live. Keen, sarcastic, and for all that warm-hearted, Buck's teaching figure is understanding and genial—even while refusing to pardon the unpardonable. His protagonist is as wooly-headed as most of us, but withal wanting to know the truth—especially if it allows him to understand the woman he loves. As brilliant a guide for the perplexed as this age is capable of producing.—CHARLES COULOMBE, author of *Puritan's Empire* and *Everyman Today Call Rome*

*The Gentle Traditionalist* is a book with a "strange magic," like unto the Ireland it loves and mourns. With unforgettable images and a wry sense of humor, Buck unfolds a tale of whimsical fantasy, melancholy realism, and supernatural joy, ever so gently exposing the intolerance and incoherence of the New Secular Religion that is destroying Ireland today, just as it has destroyed every culture that has surrendered to it. The remedy to this scourge is not "Christianity lite" or the "spirit of Vatican II," but the *real* religion that raised Western civilization to its glory: the traditional Catholic Faith. Buck's deftly-reasoned post-modern apologetic for full-blooded Catholicism—a Syllabus of Errors in narrative form, a rousing hymn to "meaning, grace, beauty, *life*"—will be salutary for those who are still wandering and for those already arrived in port.—PETER KWASNIEWSKI, Wyoming Catholic College; author of *Resurgent in the Midst of Crisis*

*The Gentle Traditionalist* is a book long overdue. Writing with great wisdom, insight, and a most warm sense of humor, Roger Buck offers us a contemplation of the religious predicaments of our time in the spirit of Chesterton and Belloc. He takes on everything—from the reforms of Vatican II to the New Age, from the postmodern religion of science to the fallout from agnostic ennui—in a charming (and disarming) manner sure to delight readers already participant in Christian tradition, and to prove at least intriguing to those who are not. It is a wonderful book.—MICHAEL MARTIN, author of *The Submerged Reality: Sophiology and the Turn to a Poetic Metaphysics*

This is a beautiful, moving book drawn from Roger Buck's own experience of both the sacramental and secular perspectives. He has managed to explain these perspectives, but perhaps more importantly, he has enabled us to *feel* the consequences. To read this work was a joy, and I thank the author for helping me realize that, despite the passing of three generations and 150 years in the Irish-Australian diaspora, my heart is still Irish. I can still be moved with longing for what sacramental Christianity has to offer, not only in eternity, but also for the here and now.—GERARD O'SHEA, University of Notre Dame, Australia; author of *As I Have Loved You*

This striking novel by Roger Buck, set in Ireland, is composed with extraordinary sensitivity and insight. The Catholic Church is travelling through a time of seemingly paralysing crisis. It has lost touch not only with its roots but also with its unique sacramental nature. However, periods of crisis can, with the help of the Holy Spirit, create openings—and one prays that the Church will again become an instrument of salvation, prayer and God-centred worship. We are indebted to Roger Buck for his spiritual clarity and striking mental lucidity.—COLIN MAWBY KSG, Choral Director of Radio Telefis Eireann (RTÉ), Artistic Director Emeritus of Ireland's National Chamber Choir

An unusual book: part love story, part theological dialog. But more importantly, its author, Roger Buck, is that altogether too rare Catholic

who understands the importance of what I have called the geo-cultural forces that have shaped the modern world—thinking here especially of how Anglo-American Protestant capitalist culture has waged a relentless war against Catholic culture everywhere in the world—and pointedly in Ireland, a country which the author loves and where he sets his story. Unless Catholics come to recognize the historical place of the Church and Catholic culture in the world, as also the forces that work against her, then whatever our personal piety may be, our action in the public square will be at worst, counterproductive, at best confused.
—THOMAS STORCK, author of *From Christendom to Americanism and Beyond*

*The Gentle Traditionalist* is a tremendous book: moving and humorous, opening up the most profound issues, engaging the most strident of polemics with the lightest touch. Ireland's place in the English-speaking world, the revolutions and counter-revolutions of the Enlightenment and the modern era, and the human weakness and divine resilience of the Catholic Church, are the book's themes. But it remains for all that an easy read, above all a gentle appeal to those outside the Church to reconsider the hostility which, for so many, is now an unthinking, bred-in-the-bone prejudice. Today it is hard to know what to say to the sincere enquirer, when the Church appears to send out such mixed signals and internal disputes take up so much of her time and energy. Roger Buck is to be congratulated for making the case for the Church at this moment of confusion. For Christ has not ceased to be our one hope, the *Spes Unica*; and the Church is today, more than ever, the only path back from the barbarism that seems to be engulfing the West.
—JOSEPH SHAW, President of the Latin Mass Society of England and Wales

# The
# Gentle
# Traditionalist

# THE GENTLE
## Traditionalist

CLARIFICATIONS PROVIDED
QUESTIONS ANSWERED
ARGUMENTS ASSERTED

*All in the*
 *Most Gentle Manner*
*humanly possible*

**(Entirely *Free of Charge*
to all *Genuine Enquirers*)**

ROGER BUCK

# The Gentle Traditionalist

*A Catholic Fairy-tale
from Ireland*

Angelico Press

First published in the USA and UK
by Angelico Press
© Roger Buck 2015

For information, address:
Angelico Press
4709 Briar Knoll Dr.
Kettering, OH 45429
angelicopress.com

ISBN 978-1-62138-157-0 (pbk)
ISBN 978-1-62138-158-7 (cloth)
ISBN 978-1-62138-159-4 (ebook)

Cover Design: Michael Schrauzer

# Acknowledgments

FIRST and foremost, I thank my beloved wife Kim. Her wisdom, love and unstinting faith in me have immeasurably nourished all my writing. However, with this particular book, her contribution was notable in other ways. Let me explain. This book *erupted* out of me in an extraordinary creative process over ten short weeks in the spring of 2015. Excited by my rapidly developing manuscript, Kim suggested a number of small touches, which leant life and colour to the story. In addition to Kim, I also thank my courageous daughter Mary, who was ever in my heart during this time and will always be the light and joy of my life.

Georg Nicolaus, who did much to guide me from the New Age movement to the Holy Church, is to be thanked for profound friendship, help and illuminating conversations over nearly three decades now. I also owe more to Romany Buck than I can say: love and support in countless ways (including inspired "pixieness"!).

Likewise, I thank Mark Anderson for his never-failing belief in me, despite our very different visions. Mark designed and sustains the website that launched my writing. That act of love has transformed my life and it remains doubtful whether this book would have been written without it.

I also thank John Riess and James Wetmore at Angelico Press who discovered my writing on the web and believed in me. It is a great privilege to be published by Angelico. More than just a publishing house, it strikes me as an inspired beacon of light in a darkening world. I pray it receives all the support it so richly deserves and needs.

I am also indebted to Dr. Rik Van Nieuwenhove for aspects of chapter 6. Long years ago, his memorable lectures on St. Anselm at Mary Immaculate College, Limerick, Ireland planted seeds that have ripened therein. Also, the unusual timepiece in this story derives from very similar ones in real life. The people manufacturing them deserve a plug: http://popepiusclock.com.

There has also been great inspiration and support from my Spanish friends. ¡Muchas gracias, Luis María Santamaria Lancho, Maria Cifuentes, Antonio Romero, Luis Flamenco! I also must pay tribute to the Institute of Christ the King whose wondrous Latin liturgy has nurtured my soul whilst living in four different countries: France, Spain, England and Ireland.

And, in alphabetical order, I express my heartfelt gratitude to Manuela Andolina, Nathan Banks, Leon Crisp, John Halloran, Fr. Dan Horgan, Sue and Tony Mathews, Michael Martin, Marc Potiez, and Siri Restrick, whilst I thank many other old friends silently in my heart.

Having named the living, it is time to credit the dead. My late beloved father, John Buck, gave so very much to me. But there are also three deceased friends I never met: Valentin Tomberg, Hilaire Belloc, and L. Brent Bozell, Jr. Their writings have so enriched my soul that I am incapable of regarding them as anything other than cherished companions and mentors.

Finally, I wish to acknowledge the faithful in my rural Irish parish of Upper Badoney. Whilst this book invokes the serious problems often occasioned by the new liturgy, our priest is living proof that the Novus Ordo can be celebrated with beauty, dignity, and reverence. Meanwhile, the remarkable piety, humanity and kindness of his parishioners in this materialistic age moves my heart no end. Whether it is seeing the Irish regularly praying by their parents' graves or witnessing their continued devotion to family and friends, I feel an uncommon wholesomeness in my village that seems immensely significant to me. I have long wanted to stand up and exclaim: "You people are wonderful!" And now I have.

# The Option
# of an Introduction

STRICTLY speaking, there is no need for this introduction.

This short novel is primarily a dialogue of ideas. And I crafted it to make the ideas easily accessible. Thus, I wanted the book to stand alone, without supplementary explanation. That being said, my story takes place in Ireland and touches on elements of Irish history—as well as the oft-forgotten Catholic Counter-Revolution—that may be obscure to some readers. Still, these details are secondary and I trust that the careful reader, even if ignorant of history, can understand the story without this introduction.

After further reflection, though, it seems appropriate to say something for those who know little of these things. Thus, I offer you, reader, the opportunity to either skip ahead to the good stuff or to familiarize yourself, first, with a little of the past. (Along the way, I also provide a bit of my own personal background—which explains why I believe this history matters.)

Let me begin with Counter-Revolution. Different people mean different things by this term. For some, it primarily signifies violent resistance to the 1789 French Revolution and other revolutions that broke out in Catholic countries later (such as Spain, Italy, various nations in Latin America, and elsewhere). Indeed, in Ireland, as we shall see, there were numerous Catholic uprisings against the Protestant British which, it seems to me, also possess a counter-revolutionary spirit, even if they are not usually designated as such. In all instances, Catholics took up arms to defend their culture against the onslaught of forces owing to revolution, whether it was the original Protestant revolution or later ones.

However, a much broader—and more profound—understanding of Catholic Counter-Revolution is possible. As the devout

Joseph de Maistre wrote after the 1789 revolution, which killed the French Royal family, not to mention scores of thousands from every other class:

> The return to order will not be painful, because it will be natural and because it will be favoured by a secret force whose action is wholly creative. We will see precisely the opposite of what we have seen. Instead of these violent commotions, painful divisions, and perpetual and desperate oscillations, a certain stability, an indefinable peace, a universal well-being will announce the presence of sovereignty.
>
> This is the great truth with which the French cannot be too greatly impressed: the restoration of the monarchy, what they call the Counter-Revolution, will not be a *contrary revolution*, but the *contrary of revolution*.[1]

Thus, for de Maistre, a genuine Counter-Revolution is not effected through violence. For this would mean nothing more than a second revolution of the same substance as the first. For him—we repeat—a genuine Counter-Revolution will be "precisely the opposite of what we have seen," entailing "a secret force whose action is wholly creative."

Personally, all this puts me in mind of prayer and the Holy Sacraments of the Church—as well as sacramentals like the Rosary, Holy Water and consecrating the home to the Sacred Heart of Jesus (all of which are fundamental to the Catholic culture which once thoroughly pervaded Ireland). De Maistre, I am sure, would concur: he was instrumental in forging a profoundly Catholic counter-revolutionary current of thinkers and pious people who desperately sought an alternative to the secular, materialistic ethos that has now triumphed in today's world.

Prayer and sacrifice, then, are key things to Catholic Counter-Revolution and what the Gentle Traditionalist, my protagonist in this book, stands for.

We will not further engage the tension between de Maistre's view and the tragic warfare that has rarely, but occasionally, char-

---

[1] Joseph de Maistre, *Considerations on France*, trans. Richard LeBrun (Cambridge: Cambridge University Press, 1994), 105.

acterized Counter-Revolution. Let us simply say that Counter-Revolution entailed *intense resistance from Catholics who could not bear the suppression of their culture.* At its best, there was intensity of prayer and sacrifice rather than intensity of violence. Does this mean all the Counter-Revolutionary wars were unjustified then? How can any mere human say? Only God can judge what Catholics in the past went through and what they did, whilst everything precious to them was being destroyed.

But, if, good reader, all this sounds exotic to you, this brings us neatly to the point of this introduction: I know these things are now strange and unfamiliar to many people, in Anglo-American culture particularly.

Indeed, my life's experience points me to this conclusion: English and American culture has conspired—sometimes innocently, sometimes not—to ensure these matters remain obscure within the Anglosphere. The Catholic Mystery is simply blanked-out by the vast majority of our Anglo-American media. And it is Anglo-American media—from British rock to Hollywood to what the French call GAFA (Google-Apple-Facebook-Amazon)—that now dominates the planet.

If my criticisms of Anglo-American culture seem sharp or excessive, I hope to be granted a little leeway, inasmuch as I stem from this sphere myself. For my roots are both in England and America. My parents were English, but I was born in America. I grew up in both countries. Thus, I sometimes say that I am quintessentially Anglo-American.

And in my case, at least, my Anglo-American heritage worked to *utterly obscure the true nature of the Catholic Church.* I hardly think I am alone in this. Like most of my fellow Brits and Americans, my patrimony is mainly Protestant, even if I was not raised as one. Still, nearly everything I experienced of Christianity *was* Protestant, including the ranting televangelists I saw on my American TV. Frankly, it all seemed dull, limited and literalist to me. I never realized that Christianity encompassed *so much more* than this. Only much later did I see that Protestantism accounted for less than thirty percent of Christianity worldwide—far smaller than the vast sacramental territory occupied by Catholicism and Eastern Orthodoxy. Of course, I had not the slightest idea what a Sacrament even was(!) nor indeed of many other sublime things preserved in Catholic worship.

Knowing nothing of the Catholic Mystery, I sought out New Age mysteries: the thrill of the esoteric. Again, I do not think I am alone in this. In England and America particularly, many spiritually sensitive folk—seeing nothing sublime in a Christianity they find boring—turn to the New Age. They are good souls, represented in this book by the character of Anna. At any event, I spent nearly twenty years in the emerging New Age subculture of the 1980s and 90s. (This included some two and a half years living at Findhorn in Scotland, probably the most well-known New Age community in the world.)

Just before my thirty-fourth birthday, however, I had a conversion experience, the fruits of which would eventually liberate me from my accumulated layers of New Age ideology. We cannot go into that here, although I discuss it in my upcoming book *Cor Jesu Sacratissimum*. (I also blog about it at a website of the same name: http://corjesusacratissimum.org.)

Rather, my point is that *my Anglo-American background blinded me* to what has become the greatest joy of my life—participation in the Holy Mystery of the Church. What obscured my vision was both the Protestant images (and stereotypes) of Christianity I saw, as well as the secular and New Age ideology which now permeates the Anglosphere. All this rendered Catholicism opaque to me, as it does to countless other Anglophones.

It may help if I add that my English parents bore significant anti-Catholic bias, rampant in my mother, but also subtly present in my gentle father. After my conversion, I tried to understand how their prejudice arose. I concluded it was not their fault. Their parents and grandparents had been thoroughly marinated in a widespread Nineteenth-century British anti-Catholicism whose effects, whilst attenuated today, subtly and insidiously persist. This, too, is addressed in my upcoming book. Here I simply say that my explorations have convinced me that, decades ago, Hilaire Belloc fingered the predicament all too well:

> With the exception of Ireland, the area covered by English speech—that is, Great Britain, the white Dominions, and

the United States—have *a character of their own* so far as the Catholic Church is concerned.

The English-speaking world, though now morally broken up, had *a common root.* Its institutions, at their origin, sprang from the *English Protestant Seventeenth Century* [italics mine].

The American social groups arose for the most part as emigrant colonies with a definitely religious origin, and nearly all of them with an origin strongly anti-Catholic. In England, Scotland, and Wales the Catholic Church had been defeated by 1605. . . . It was by 1688 no more than a seventh or an eighth of England in numbers, much less of Scotland, and in both countries failing.

It dwindled after 1688 to a tiny fragment—about one percent—and that pitiful atom was of no account in the national life nor of any effect on national institutions. From such a source flowed first the colonial system of America, next that of the Dominions. Of course, so general a statement needs modification. South Africa was . . . Dutch; the New World had Dutch origins in one of its states and Catholic traditions in two others. But, in outline, the generalization is true.

The stuff of all this culture was one from which Catholicism had been driven out, and till the mid-Nineteenth Century the United States, Great Britain and her Colonies had little need to reckon with the Faith within their own boundaries.

In our own time all that has largely changed. The chief agent of the change has been the Irish people dispersed by the famine. They brought a large Catholic body into England, Australasia, Canada, and America.[2]

Belloc is saying, then, that—Catholic Ireland excepted—the cultural roots of virtually the entire Anglosphere are thoroughly pervaded by Protestantism. Moreover, before Irish immigration began, Belloc notes how the Anglosphere was severed from Catholicism in a manner different from great Protestant societies

---

[2] Hilaire Belloc, *Survivals and New Arrivals* (Rockford, IL: TAN, 1992), 16–17, 13.

elsewhere. For example, German and Dutch culture always had to contend with significant Catholic populations, whether in Catholic Austria or Bavaria or in the large proportion of Catholics remaining in Holland and Belgium. Thus, Catholicism *remained familiar* to those speaking German and Dutch, whereas to English-speakers it became remote (not to mention endlessly ridiculed). Belloc argues this had significant impact for almost the entire English-speaking world:

> Where the character of Catholicism is familiar to all, holding an ancient historic position, and where large Catholic societies of the same blood and speech lie just over the frontiers . . . *Catholic literature, ideas, history are known.*
>
> *But in the English-speaking world it is otherwise* [italics mine]. There Catholicism re-entered late as an alien phenomenon after the character of society had become "set" in an anti-Catholic mould. There all national literature, traditions, law and especially history were . . . long settled in the anti-Catholic mood before the first recrudescence of Catholicism appeared.
>
> Therefore it is inevitable that the Catholic body within this English-speaking world should breathe an air which is not its own and should be more affected by a non-Catholic or anti-Catholic spirit than could be possible in the other Protestant nations wherein an ancient Catholic culture exists with unbroken traditions. . . .
>
> Similarly the great body of [continental] literature in the Catholic culture is closed to these minorities of Catholics in the English-speaking world. They have no powerful daily press. They get nearly all their news and more than half their ideas from papers anti-Catholic in direction. The books which make the mind of the nation help to make the mind of its Catholic minority—and that literature is, in bulk, vividly anti-Catholic.[3]

It was only after my conversion that I could fully appreciate the truth here. For I spent some years living in culturally Catholic countries—Ireland, Spain, France—lands steeped in Catholic

---

[3] Ibid., 18–19.

thinking, literature, arts and more. These were, in short, countries where the Catholic Mystery *is publicly visible* in a way very, very different to England or America.

For me, all this confirmed Belloc's view of the tunnel vision of the formerly Protestant, now secular Anglosphere. Tunnel vision: I recall something on the English Internet, where the writer spoke of how the Roman Catholic Church had once been the "mainstream" church of the West. French or Spanish writers would never say this. To them, it is obvious the Catholic Church has never ceased being the dominant form of Christianity in the world! But in the Anglosphere it is all-too-easily assumed: mainstream Christianity = Protestant.

Anglo-American culture has robbed people of understanding the Catholic world, which dwarfs it. Yet we now face a grave situation whereby Anglo-American culture dominates the planet.

All this has been poignant and painful for me since coming back to live in the northwest of Ireland, just over two years ago. I am gravely concerned for the fate of Catholic Ireland, overwhelmed as it is by the two cultures from which I stem. Daily, I ask how the Irish spiritual genius can be preserved, so that Ireland does not simply become a second-rate clone of the liberal Anglo-American world.

Some may wonder if I excessively blame my own countries of origin. What of homegrown Irish cultural and political leaders who have steered Ireland on her present course? What, for example, of current Prime Minister Enda Kenny, who (against electoral promises and without a referendum!) recently legalized abortion in Ireland?

Of course, Kenny and Irish folk of his ilk must be held accountable! And, admittedly, there is a native Irish liberal tradition (even if much of that owes to the small Anglo-Irish Protestant population that remained after Ireland achieved independence from Britain in 1922). Obviously, there are also other factors destroying Irish Catholic culture. Most notably, the appalling sexual abuse that occurred in Ireland—which we consider in these pages—has taken its toll. Clearly, an entire complex of issues is at work, rather than simply "Anglo-Americanization."

Nonetheless, it is often remarked how much *the young* have

transformed Irish culture, abandoning the "faith of their fathers." And the young—along with by now middle-aged Irish elites—have grown up in an age wherein Ireland became awash in British and American media like never before. Thus, for example, the rock stars who pervaded these generations' formative years were, above all, British, but also American. They were not, however, Italian, French or Spanish! Being British and American myself, I cannot help but feel acutely conscious of how much my own culture has thoroughly pervaded this country. Thus, I also sadly note that the majority of newspapers the Irish read are of British origin. And, on the rare occasions I watch Irish television, something hits me in the guts: just how many English or American productions I see. It runs the gamut from talk shows and Hollywood blockbusters to soap operas and cartoons: everything from *Oprah* to *The Simpsons*.

I am hardly alone in these concerns. Rachel Shearer at the internet site IrishCentral writes:

> There are many American traditions that we slowly adopt over the years. Nickelodeon had a lot to answer for in the late 1990s as Irish children began to develop inexplicably strong U.S. accents and the country was met with an epidemic of juvenile eye-rolling and answering "whatever" to almost everything. I have strong memories of saying "duh!" about 400 times a day thanks to Sabrina the Teenage Witch and thinking I was the coolest kid on the block for having learned this spicy, exotic lingo.[4]

"Duh" and "whatever" are obvious manifestations. More subtly, I maintain, contemporary Irish cultural attitudes owe far more to the liberalism stemming from London and Hollywood than is often acknowledged. Very recently, Ireland voted for same-sex "marriage" and the yes vote was carried by the young. In France and Spain, I noticed a marked difference. There the Anglo-American influence is comparatively much reduced and even with the

---

[4] "Zip codes, TV shows and brunch—Ireland is a land of copycats"; http://www.irishcentral.com/news/irishvoice/Zip-codes-TV-shows-and-brunch—Ireland-is-a-land-of-copycats.html. Accessed July 28, 2015.

young, there are mighty movements against same-sex "marriage" that would confound the liberalized youth of Ireland today.

Having tarried with these personal observations, it is time to focus on our main task: supplying a little Irish and counter-revolutionary context for those who may lack it. The easiest way to do that is to provide a small timeline.

Here, my approach has been to simplify things for a general audience. The dates I provide may also seem scattered, even idiosyncratic. My intent, in this short space, however, is modest. I merely mean to *evoke* some long-forgotten history. What follows, then, is highly selective: I have simply chosen some dates which supply readers with a little historical context for the short novel that follows. Not all are key to my little tale, but even the less important ones may help to conjure up Irish history as well as a traditionalist counter-revolutionary culture that sorely needs remembering.

We commence by traveling back in time nearly sixteen hundred years:

432: Traditional date of St Patrick's arrival in Ireland. Gaelic civilization converted to Christianity with extraordinary ease and rapidity.

476: Fall of last Roman Emperor in the West. This date is often used to mark the collapse of Roman civilization and the beginning of the Dark Ages.

500–800: Golden age of Irish Christianity. Whilst culture and literacy crumbles on the continent, Irish saints and scholars copy Christian manuscripts and protect the faith, later sending missionaries to evangelize Europe.

1000–1500: High Middle Ages. Catholicism flourishes across Western Europe. Whilst Ireland is no longer unique in Europe, her ecclesiastical life remains rich and extensive.

1169: Forces from Britain begin to invade Ireland, subjugating her to the kings of England.

1517: Martin Luther begins the *Protestant Revolution* at Wittenberg.

**Late 1520s onwards**: Protestantisation of England. Processes commence whereby Henry VIII of England, unable to end his marriage, declares himself head of a new Church of England. Persecution of Catholics begins, including dissolution—looting and confiscation—of the monasteries of Britain and Ireland. Centuries of monastic life in Britain and Ireland are thereby ended.

**1545**: The *Council of Trent* is convened, pioneering the Catholic Counter-Reformation.

**1593–1601**: Nine Years War in Ireland. Hugh O'Neil leads Catholic armies, defeated by Queen Elizabeth I.

**1600 onwards**: Rise of de-christianised, rationalist, Enlightenment philosophy exemplified by Bacon, Descartes, Locke, Hume, Voltaire, Kant.

**1603**: James I comes to English Throne. He commences *Ulster Plantation* whereby nearly 500,000 acres of land in the north of Ireland are confiscated from Irish Catholics and given to English and Scottish Protestant settlers. Origins of present day conflict in Northern Ireland.

**1641**: Dispossessed in Ulster rise up against British rule, leading to *Irish Catholic Confederation,* which succeeds in retaking most of Ireland. At least 2000 Protestants killed by Catholics.

**1649–1653**: *Oliver Cromwell* arrives from England. His armies massacre up to 500,000 people or one quarter of the Irish population. Most of the remaining Catholics are stripped of their land, often forced to survive on small plots of land, poor soil and the humble potato. This enforced reliance on the potato will have terrifying consequences two hundred years later. Increased Catholic repression follows, with priests expelled from Ireland on threat of execution if they return. Penal laws commence in earnest with intent to wipe out Catholicism.

**1670s**: Beginnings in Paray-le-Monial, France, of the preeminent cult of the Catholic Counter-Revolution: *Devotion to* the *Sacred Heart of Jesus*. St. Margaret Mary Alacoque has visions of the Sacred Heart calling for the public devotion.

**1690**: *Battle of the Boyne*. Further Catholic uprising defeated by the British.

**1789–1815**: The *French Revolution* and ensuing Napoleonic wars devastate Europe. In the words of Christopher Dawson: "In sheer material destruction of monasteries and churches, in confiscation of property and abrogation of privileges, the Age of the Revolution far surpassed that of the Reformation; it was in fact a second Reformation, but a frankly anti-religious one."[5]

In France, the Sacred Heart is taken up as the Counter-Revolutionary emblem *par excellence* during this period.

**1798**: Another major Irish rebellion, defeated by the growing might of the British Empire.

**1829**: *Catholic Emancipation* permits Catholicism to flourish again in Ireland. Catholics now freely build thousands of Catholic churches across the island.

**1830**: Our Lady appears weeping in the *Rue du Bac*, Paris. She laments the Cross being overthrown and the destruction of the French monarchy. From here will come both the Miraculous Medal and incredible impetus for the culture of Counter Revolution.

**1833–1839**: *First Carlist War* (of three) in Spain against government espousing French revolutionary principles.

**1845–49**: Irish potato crop is blighted. In the famine that ensues, population of Ireland is reduced by up to thirty-five percent, either through death or mass immigration. Yet mass Irish immigration reintroduces Catholicism to the Anglosphere.

**1846**: Apparition of *Our Lady of La Salette*, France, again weeping for de-christianised humanity.

---

[5] Christopher Dawson, *The Gods of Revolution* (Washington, DC: CUA Press, 2015), 116.

**1860–1870**: Italian annexation of Rome and Papal States, resisted by a multinational army summoned by Pope Bl. Pius IX. Three thousand Irishmen volunteer—despite the British government threatening them with prosecution if they enlist in the Pope's forces! (Conversely, the British government raises no objection to those joining the conquering Italian armies.)[6]

**1870**: Birth of the Anglo-French writer Hilaire Belloc, who will initiate a profoundly influential current of English Catholic literature and political theory (Distributism).

**1874**: Birth of G. K. Chesterton, who, inspired by Belloc, will convert to Catholicism and vigorously campaign for Distributism. Chesterton's writings inspire countless numbers and help to convert many, including C. S. Lewis, Marshall McLuhan and Graham Greene.

**1879**: *Our Lady of Knock* appears to fifteen people in a pouring rainstorm in County Mayo, Ireland. Wearing a golden crown, her feet are slightly raised above the earth. Beneath them, the ground is dry.

**1916**: *Easter Rising* in Dublin. Catholic rebels commandeer key buildings in the city. *Patrick Pearse* proclaims Irish Republic, free from Britain. Rebellion is suppressed and rebel leaders immediately executed by the British—except for *Éamon de Valera* who, mysteriously, is spared.

**1917**: *Communist Revolution* in Russia, followed by genocide of monumental proportions.

**1919**: Mounting IRA violence in Ireland. Britain dispatches brutal reserve forces to Ireland. Nicknamed the "Black and Tans," they achieve lasting notoriety for the terror of their reprisal.

**1920**: "Black and Tans" sack Cork, December 11, looting and burning a large section of the city centre.

---

[6] Charles A. Coulombe, *The Pope's Legion* (New York: Palgrave Macmillan, 2008), 55, 59.

**1922**: After six years of unrest in Ireland, treaty establishes Irish Free State in the South. Northern six counties remain under British government. In the decades ensuing, Éamon de Valera will become the most prominent of the new nation's leaders.

**1937**: Éamon de Valera, prime minister of Ireland, drafts Irish constitution, whose preamble begins with acknowledging Irish "obligations to our Divine Lord, Jesus Christ." The new constitution is passed by popular vote.

**Late 1940s onwards**: Rise of television, portable transistor radios, rock and roll.

**1960s–1970s**: Sexual Revolution, rise of drug use and crime rates, and other sweeping cultural changes in the West. Widespread liberalization of laws controlling divorce, abortion and pornography. Ireland—to her critics—remains "culturally backwards."

**1961**: Years after countless commercial television stations emerge in America, Ireland starts transmitting a single public television station. President Éamon de Valera expresses prescience regarding television in the opening broadcast: "Like atomic energy, it can be used for incalculable good, but it can also do irreparable harm. Never before was there in the hands of men an instrument so powerful to influence the thoughts and actions of the multitude. . . . It can lead through demoralization to decadence and disillusion."[7]

**1962–1965**: *Vatican II* initiates sweeping changes in the Catholic Church, which only accelerate in the years following the Council.

**Late 1960s–mid '70s**: New Mass in vernacular languages becomes widely introduced. Time of vast dissent in the Church. Liberal theologians protest *Humanae Vitae* encyclical on birth control—and much more. Mass exodus of priests and nuns from the Church. Collapse of vocations.

---

[7] Quoted in Robert J. Savage, *Irish Television: The Political and Social Origins* (Westport, CT: Praeger Publishers, 1996), xi.

Rapid decline of confession and, less rapidly, other Sacraments. The few remaining traditionalists feel persecuted on every front.

**1978 onward**: After ascending the Throne of Peter, *St. John Paul II* begins to halt chaos in the Church, disciplining rebel theologians, stemming the haemorrhage of the priesthood and slowly pioneering a return to orthodoxy with countless measures, including a new *Catechism of the Catholic Church* and indults to permit the traditional Latin Mass again.

**1986**: Referendum to allow divorce in Ireland defeated by thumping two-thirds margin.

**1990s onward**: Monstrous sexual abuse by a small proportion of priests and their victims' agony come to light. Scandals rock the Church in Ireland, America and certain other countries.

**1995**: Ireland legalizes divorce by the narrowest of margins: 49.7 percent of voters still say no.

**Late 1990s onward**: Rise of the "Celtic Tiger" in Ireland. Rapid economic growth ensues as a result of deregulation, newly established transnational corporations and stimulus from the European Union. Ireland goes from being one of the poorest countries in Europe to amongst the richest. A modern, "globalized" Ireland emerges.

**2007**: Benedict XVI issues the Motu Proprio *Summorum Pontificum* to fully liberate the Tridentine Latin Mass.

**2008**: Collapse of "Celtic Tiger," amidst longstanding government irresponsibility and global economic downturn.

**2013**: Irish government legalizes abortion.

**2015**: Twenty years after she approved divorce by the narrowest of margins, Ireland approves same-sex "marriage" by a far more substantial one.

Before closing, I should like to venture a few last things about Ireland. My debt to this ancient Christian land is enormous. How much unfathomable treasure I have drawn from her profound wells of Christianity! And how my heart has been warmed by the uncommon kindness of her people! I have lived in seven countries in all, and Irish society still strikes me, even today, as the most human.

All this is beyond anything I can possibly express here. (I do say more in my upcoming, larger book.) Suffice it to say, I have a love affair with Ireland and I consider this little book a *love letter*: a valentine for Catholic Ireland.

However, it is not enough to wax maudlin. True love entails more than sentimentality. It demands care, compassion and effort for the beloved who suffers. Today, the Ireland that I love suffers greatly.

I write these words in the latter half of 2015, as this country anticipates a milestone in her history: the one-hundredth anniversary of the 1916 Easter Rising, which led to the modern Irish Republic.

Today, secular Ireland appears distinctly uncomfortable with this centenary. There are different factors for this. Some strike me as noble in essence, others less so. On the noble side, some feel the Rising was not a Just War. They also rightly recoil at the terrible violence committed by the IRA in recent decades and start to wonder whether the 1916 revolutionaries—including the aforementioned Patrick Pearse and Éamon de Valera—might be little more than terrorists. (Truly, their attitudes would shock many of my fellow Americans who never entertain such thoughts about their own founding revolutionaries—even though the Irish revolution was far less bloody than the American one.)

Less nobly, modern Ireland uses different routes to circumvent the "problem of 1916." One route is to dismiss the rebels as Catholic fanatics, whilst another is precisely the opposite: to claim the revolutionaries were, in reality, more groovy, "Progressive" and multicultural than the facts attest. Admittedly, Pearse's words in 1916 occasionally lend themselves to this sort of interpretation. However, the more I study the Rising, the more clearly I see what R. F. Forster writes in his historical masterpiece, *Modern Ireland*:

> An intrinsic component of the insurrection (for all the pluralist window-dressing of the Proclamation issued by

Pearse) was the strain of mystic Catholicism identifying the Irish soul as Catholic and Gaelic.[8]

This notion is only strengthened by what transpired after the Rising. Upon achieving independence, Ireland opted—with vast popular support—for a far less secular system than Britain, one in which Church and State were interwoven in ways unthinkable in other English-speaking countries. Thus, for example, new laws were passed—again with democratic support—promoting tighter censorship and restricting divorce and the sale of contraceptives, amidst other measures favoured by the Catholic morality of the vast majority of its citizens. As noted above, a new constitution was voted in, which rooted ultimate authority not simply in the "consent of the governed," but rather in the Triune Christian God:

> In the Name of the Most Holy Trinity, from Whom is all authority and to Whom, as our final end, all actions both of men and States must be referred,
> We, the people of Éire,
> Humbly acknowledging all our obligations to our Divine Lord, Jesus Christ, Who sustained our fathers through centuries of trial,
> Gratefully remembering their heroic and unremitting struggle to regain the rightful independence of our Nation,
> And seeking to promote the common good, with due observance of Prudence, Justice and Charity, so that the dignity and freedom of the individual may be assured, true social order attained, the unity of our country restored, and concord established with other nations,
> Do hereby adopt, enact, and give to ourselves this Constitution.

Six years after drafting the above, Éamon de Valera gave a famous speech, outlining the vision of Ireland which animated him long before the 1916 Rising:

> The ideal Ireland that we would have, the Ireland that we dreamed of, would be the home of a people who valued

[8] R. F. Forster, *Modern Ireland, 1600–1972* (London: Penguin Books, 1989), 479.

material wealth only as a basis for right living, of a people who, satisfied with frugal comfort, devoted their leisure to the things of the spirit—a land whose countryside would be bright with cosy homesteads, whose fields and villages would be joyous with the sounds of industry, with the romping of sturdy children, the contest of athletic youths and the laughter of happy maidens, whose firesides would be forums for the wisdom of serene old age. The home, in short, of a people living the life that God desires that men should live.

With the tidings that make such an Ireland possible, St. Patrick came to our ancestors fifteen hundred years ago promising happiness here no less than happiness hereafter. It was the pursuit of such an Ireland that later made our country worthy to be called the island of saints and scholars. It was the idea of such an Ireland—happy, vigorous, spiritual—that fired the imagination of our poets; that made successive generations of patriotic men give their lives to win religious and political liberty; and that will urge men in our own and future generations to die, if need be, so that these liberties may be preserved.

What can I say? It is impossible to imagine any politician being elected today on a platform for a life of the spirit "satisfied with frugal comfort!" Yet Catholic Ireland repeatedly re-elected the man: He spent thirty-four years as either prime minister or president of the country.

Thus, for decades, Ireland swam against the tide of English-speaking culture elsewhere. All this started to unravel by the late 1960s. Obviously, increasingly globalized media and the sweeping cultural changes elsewhere in the West played a part. Personally, however, I do not believe the great transformation in the Catholic Church during the 1960s can be exonerated here. What would have happened in Ireland, had the Church retained reverence in her liturgy and staunch adherence to devotions like the Sacred Heart, benediction, Corpus Christi processions, holy water in the home, etc.? It is a question well worth pondering. (Especially as—I increasingly suspect—the old liturgy *strengthened* the clergy in a manner the new does not.)

At any rate, despite immense cultural and ecclesiastical changes worldwide, Ireland remained, initially, *a place apart*. How much that is so can be glimpsed from a 1974 survey,[9] which found over ninety percent of Catholics still attended Mass weekly and nearly forty-seven percent went to confession once a month, whereas ninety-seven percent prayed daily. Seventy-five percent put up holy pictures or statues in their homes. Moreover, around a quarter of the population went to Mass more than once a week and a similar proportion confessed once a week or more!

Today, however, all is "changed, changed utterly" in Ireland— to borrow Yeats' famous refrain regarding 1916. Ireland has largely, if not completely, succumbed to the materialistic values that the 1916 revolutionaries fought to preserve her from. For, as Desmond Ryan writes, Patrick Pearse was concerned that:

> The [Irish] people had lost their souls and were being vulgarized, commercialized, anxious only to imitate the material prosperity of England.[10]

Pearse was hardly alone in this. Much of the Rising's impetus stemmed from the rebels' belief that, without it, the soul of Ireland would slowly be extinguished by British governance, British capitalism and British education.

I realize much that I say here and elsewhere in this book will be contentious in Ireland today, even inflammatory. Assuming it achieves any notice here, I expect to be hated for this book in certain quarters of modern Ireland. If so, the things I would be hated for are mainly things the majority of Irish people held sacred fifty years ago. This would simply show, then, that modern Ireland hates its own past and its own traditions, which is something immensely tragic.

There is little scope to say more. Still, as we approach the anniversary of the Rising, I pray this small book will serve notice that there are those still living in Ireland who remain wondrous

---

[9] Tom Inglis, *Moral Monopoly* (Dublin: University College Dublin Press, 1998), 17, 29.

[10] Desmond Ryan, *Remembering Sion: A Chronicle of Storm and Quiet* (London: Arthur Barker, 1934), 161.

that 1916 led to an extraordinary situation: an Irish state which firmly rejected the values of the increasingly secularized, materialistic culture elsewhere.

To my mind, the extraordinary kindness and humanness I still see in this country is inextricably connected to the Catholic culture that once thrived here. That culture—whilst fallen, with dark corners, like every culture—fostered a wholesome community spirit and charity which still persist in Ireland today, particularly in rural areas. Frankly, it takes my breath away, even though, with the ongoing destruction of that Catholic culture, there is increased greed, despair, family and social breakdown, crime, suicide and more. Many Irish people note these things and mourn for Ireland the way that I mourn.

However, I do not believe that all is yet lost. Yes, my life in Latin Catholic countries showed me how Irish Catholicism is uniquely vulnerable to the once Protestant, now secular-liberal Anglo-American tidal wave. And, of course, the immense power of global corporations and media now menace Catholic culture everywhere. Many times have I feared this small island simply does not have the wherewithal to stand against this colossus. Yet, the longer I live amidst St. Patrick's people, the more hope I gain. For I see, ever more clearly, the *profondeur* of the Catholic and Christian roots of this nation since the coming of St. Patrick 1600 years ago.

Much, much urgently needs doing to protect these roots and I hope this small book may serve to water them a little. Thus, wherever you may be in the world, dear Reader, I ask you to join with me in prayer for the soul of Ireland. For Ireland has long been a beacon of light in the Anglosphere. That light may be diminished, but it is not extinguished. Pray with me, then, I beg you, that the tree St. Patrick planted long ago may once more burst into bloom.

*Feast of St. Louis IX, King and Confessor*
25 August 2015

# I

## Opening Notes

GPL. Those are my initials. You'll hear my full name later. But let's start with those. GT—the Gentle Traditionalist—would like it that way, I think. You'll hear his real name soon too. This book isn't mine, you see. It's GT's. Without him—and what he did for me—I could never have written it.

I call it a book. But, really, I'm not sure it is a book. Not in the ordinary sense, anyway. I'll be frank with you: I'm not much of a writer. These are just some notes. Hopefully, they give you the minimum you need to make sense of my story.

That story starts in Ireland, Monaghan in the north to be precise—although I come from Winchester in England, went to Cambridge University, and work in London. I'm twenty-nine years old and I'd never been to Ireland before.

Now, it wasn't that I was especially interested in Ireland. It was SHE. She loved Ireland. And I couldn't help myself. I loved her. I always loved her. I know it sounds corny—but honestly, I think I loved her from the moment we met. It will sound even more corny when I tell you we met on Valentine's Day. I met my true love on Valentine's Day. And, later, I lost her on Valentine's Day. Cue the sad sound of violins. But I can't help it. Corny or not, it's true. And, as you'll see, it's important to my story.

Anna O'Neill is her name. With a name like that, you might think Anna was Irish. But she was English—only her father came from Ireland. She'd grown up in Liverpool, but was working as a stenographer in Cambridge when I met her. Later, we lived together in London. She always drove me crazy. In more ways than one.

Our relationship finished when Anna said she needed a year to "find herself." She'd had an inheritance which allowed her to quit the stenography. She then took off for some New Age community in Scotland where they talk to giant cabbages or something. But she didn't come back, as she'd promised. She went to Auroville in India, then Ojai and Esalen in California. It went on: two years, then three, four, five. She was having adventures all over the world. Or misadventures. She wrote me emails about burning her feet on hot coals while fire-walking in Hawaii. And she got hypothermia with Yogi Star Bear—a Native American shaman—during a "Vision-quest" in Yellowstone National Park.

I also found some time to travel. I went to Africa. What I saw appalled me. It literally gave me nightmares. Maybe I should tell you upfront: I'm pretty left-wing. To me, it's transparently obvious global capitalism has a great deal to answer for. And, after Africa, I meant to do something practical about it. By contrast, I couldn't help but judge Anna as completely impractical, frivolous even.

Neither of us started any new relationships in this time. I trust Anna implicitly in that. In her emails, she always said she still loved me, but that I shouldn't wait for her. We were just too incompatible. Our Mercuries were inconjunct. And mine was retrograde at birth. We were soul-mates, she said, but doomed by the stars.

One thing was certain: I never knew how to handle this New Age side to Anna. I always hoped she'd get over it. How could she believe all this stuff about star signs and cabbages? Not to mention karma, angels, and holistic frog-licking. Okay—I lied about the last. Still, it tells you something about my sheer frustration with this nutty side of her.

She even changed her name to Lotus Flower for a few years. But finally, she returned to stay with a friend in London for a whole summer. She was different. She seemed less crazy, more ordinary, somehow. And her name was back to Anna again. I felt relieved. Maybe all the New Age nonsense was over now.

But then she dropped the bombshell.

We could never be together, she told me. She had decided to take a vow of celibacy—be a nun. My jaw fell open. "A Buddhist nun?" I asked.

No, she said, Catholic—as in *Roman* Catholic. I couldn't believe my ears. Never in a billion years could I imagine Anna being Roman Catholic, let alone a Catholic nun!

Moreover, she wouldn't be like one of these modern nuns who wear ordinary clothes. She was going full-blast traditional. She'd found this convent of nuns in France called *Les Religieuses Victimes du Sacré Coeur*—the Religious Victims of the Sacred Heart. What a name! They were into the Mass in Latin and they were strict.

She would wear a habit, a veil, the whole bit. Anna was stunning—talk about a waste. But it was more than that, of course. I was gutted—beyond gutted. Gutted squared. Up to now, I really thought Anna and I would make it someday.

Now, she seemed further away than ever. Even if she weren't becoming a nun, much more separated us than when she was simply a New Ager. Before, we were both left-wing and we shared the same basic liberal convictions. When Anna was a New Ager, at least, she didn't think masturbation was a sin or that some people went to Hell. We both supported abortion, gay issues—stuff like that.

We were socially inclusive—and if one thing united my own secular perspectives with her New Ageism, we both agreed organised religion was pretty old-fashioned, even stupid and bigoted.

Now, Anna had suddenly developed this rigid intolerance. I really could not understand it. Yet I loved her and somehow she looked more beautiful than ever. She had this new poise and developed this enigmatic smile. It was like the Mona Lisa, I thought. But Anna was far more beautiful than the Mona Lisa! And despite her newfound rigidity, Anna actually seemed less angry than in the past. Back then, she had quite a temper. She didn't suffer fools gladly and could explode at the drop of a hat. It was weird: Now she was gentler, softer—more tolerant and intolerant at one and the same time. We still had fights, though. But Anna always apologised first—even when it was clearly my fault. Later, she went to confess it to her priest.

Finally, at the end of that summer, she left for Marseilles in France. I went to the airport with her. It was the worst day of my life. I thought she was gone forever. I didn't hear much from her after that. She was a novice—a trial nun before making vows. Still, I guess she meant to break all her worldly ties.

Then, one day at the start of February, everything changed

again. I heard she wasn't in France, but staying in a big, old farm-house outside Monaghan in Ireland. I was elated! Had she dropped the Catholic thing now, just like the New Age stuff?

No, she told me on the phone. She was still Catholic. But she wasn't sure God was calling her to be a nun. She told me the farmhouse was big and cold and empty apart from her. I told her I had two weeks' leave coming. Next day, I caught a plane to Dublin and drove up to Monaghan.

It was like old times, living under the same roof again. Except, of course, it was purely platonic. This gorgeous woman I loved. So near and yet so far. Unbearably frustrating. Still, we talked. We talked like never before.

Of course, we talked about her Catholicism. I tried to under-stand all her rigid rules. Or maybe I didn't try hard enough. Maybe I was too upset, I just wanted to protest. In any event, Anna would clam up, rather than give me rational explanations why she believed the crazy things she did. It was always "the Church teaches this." Or "the Church declared that"—back in the year 381 or something. It made me mad. How relevant was that today? And couldn't she think for herself?

Occasionally, though, she did give reasons I could understand. We were talking about Church teaching on Hell. I said it sounded pretty dour, dire, awful. She said people were already in Hell everywhere in this world, drug pushers, killers, war-mon-gerers—why should Hell stop when you kicked the bucket?

"Take Hitler," she said. "If you were responsible for killing six million Jews, five million Poles and millions more soldiers and civilians, would you expect eternal happiness, after you died?"

"No, but Christianity also talks about Hell being eternal," I objected. "A million times a million years is only the first nano-second of your infinite torment. I wouldn't wish that on anybody —not even Hitler. I can't believe in a God who is less merciful than I am."

"Hell is a mystery, a terrible mystery," she replied. "Apparently, St. John Paul II once said we cannot know for certain who will be in Hell at the end of time or indeed whether anyone will be in Hell. On the other hand: 'better to reign in Hell than serve in Heaven.'"

"What's that supposed to mean?"

"It's Milton. Satan in *Paradise Lost*. Perhaps a soul like Hitler's prefers eternal Hell to Heaven. Like I said, Hell is a mystery, unfathomable, terrible..." Her voice trailed off. Then she added, "We can't know what Heaven or Hell are really like. Not in this life. But, if you believe in an afterlife, it doesn't make sense to just suppose everyone will automatically be happy, when most people in this world are not happy."

Somehow, I could buy this. This was why Catholics talked about Purgatory and Hell. Obviously, we live on a planet of incredible suffering everywhere. Why should the next world—if there was a next world—be automatically different? At any rate, I was never against the idea of an afterlife. Indeed, I believed there must be *something* afterwards. Life couldn't be that pointless. I just couldn't see strumming a harp for eternity. Or being slowly roasted over a spit by the devil either. But if Hitler's soul was still around somewhere, I couldn't imagine he'd found eternal bliss.

No—as GT was to show me—Anna and I did share some basic beliefs. But I hardly realised this at the time. Still, I should be clear about this: I wasn't an atheist or even an agnostic. I knew there had to be *something* out there. It just didn't look like a bearded, old man in the clouds who turned himself into a baby to save me. I also didn't think the Catholic Church had some sort of monopoly on the truth. And I found Anna's attitudes towards the Church completely contradictory. For one thing, she'd gone all the way to a Latin Mass convent in Marseilles, because she couldn't bear the new liturgy. But now in Monaghan she went to an English Mass—*every single day.*

"There's no Latin Mass for miles around," she "explained."

"Then why go to an English Mass, if you don't like it?"

"The Mass is the Mass is the Mass," she said, "but you won't understand that, unless you know what the Mass is. Christ is still present there—whether you like the liturgy or not."

"You mean as something to eat?" I scoffed.

"I told you, you wouldn't understand."

I didn't. Nor could I understand why she wanted to go to a Mass in a dead language. From what I understood, the Catholic Church had changed the Mass when it liberalised itself in the

1960s. This liberalisation looked like a good thing to me. But Anna thought the changes in the Church were slowly killing it. Since the '60s, she told me, there'd been massive declines in vocations—as well as Catholic baptisms, marriages, etc. People were abandoning the Church in droves. She was particularly worried that very few people bothered with Confession anymore. The new liturgy, according to her, was a major part of the problem. Apparently, a "mystic life-force" was being drained from the Church. Anna might be a Catholic now, but she still sounded like a nutty New Ager to me.

Another point of tension between us was Ireland. She was thinking of settling down in Ireland—even though the country had little in the way of the Latin Mass. Actually, Anna always had this thing about Ireland. So this wasn't entirely new. Like I said, her father was Irish; he came from County Cork. And, as a kid, Anna went on holiday to her old grandmother in Cork. That grandmother had been very special to her and her times in Cork were magical—a respite from an unhappy childhood in Liverpool.

But now her old love of Ireland was mixed-up with her Catholicism—and a newfound Irish nationalism that, frankly, troubled me. She reeled out this version of history whereby Catholic Ireland had long been oppressed by Protestant England. It was hard for me to take. Even if the British had been terrible at times, what was the point in stirring up these ancient hatreds? Staying near Monaghan, we were only a few miles from the border with Northern Ireland. Whilst Anna deplored the terror inflicted by the Provisional IRA, she considered that border a tragic thing—a horrendous gash across the country. Both North and South desperately needed the other, she said. Cut off from each other, Ireland, according to her, could not fulfil her "spiritual calling." Whatever that meant. I just didn't get it. At any rate, Anna might be half-Irish on her father's side, but, basically, she was English. She'd grown up there, like I did. Indeed, she'd always loved England. As did I. Her newfound criticisms of England grated on my nerves.

Annoyingly, she also put down modern Ireland. Ireland, Anna said, had become too much like secular England or America. As recently as 1970, she told me, ninety per cent of the people still went to Mass every Sunday. It had dropped to something like a quarter in less than fifty years. For Anna, this was a tragedy. Also, since 1970, murder in Ireland had increased sixfold and suicide had grown by four times. Obviously, Anna linked the loss of faith to social unrest, even murder, in modern Ireland. The nation had lost what made it special, she claimed—the Catholic Church. Apparently, it was all some Anglo-American plot to turn the country into part of the capitalist West.

Weirdly, it was just the same with her old New Age stuff. Now, she really objected to holistic spirituality, calling it "pagan." It wasn't really holistic, she said. It wasn't inclusive, but exclusive. Subtly, it worked to eliminate Christ and the Cross from Western Civilisation. Much of it, she said, came from the East. But it was popularised by Anglo-American gimmicks. And now Ireland was falling for those same gimmicks.

Listening to her, it all seemed like one gigantic conspiracy against the Catholic Church in Ireland. England. America. Free-masons. President Obama. Margaret Sanger. Gloria Steinem. Hollywood. The Rolling Stones. The CIA. Helena Blavatsky. The Dalai Lama. Yogi Bear. God knows what else—maybe the Loch Ness monster, for all I knew. They were all in it together to subvert Christ's Church on earth. Arrgh. How could she take this crazy, paranoid stuff seriously?

Still, Ireland was starting to get to me, too. In a good way. The Monaghan people were friendly—sometimes astonishingly so. We broke down in Anna's old car one day. It was pouring with rain. I couldn't believe how many people stopped and helped us out. We got drenched and while one old man worked on the engine, another couple invited us back to their home to dry ourselves off and have tea. The Irish people were like that, Anna said. Ireland possessed a strange magic, I had to admit.

And maybe that Irish magic was now working on us. Because, although we fought, we also laughed a lot. In fact, I've told you the worst stuff. Because, you'll see, it's necessary to this story. But, honestly, for the most part, we were actually having a really good time during those two weeks.

So good, in fact, I started to think crazy things.

Or maybe they weren't so crazy. I could see Anna still loved me. God knew—if there was a God—I still loved her. Clearly, she was giving up the convent idea, if she wanted to live in Ireland. There was no Latin Mass convent in Ireland and no way would Anna join a modern convent. What if I were willing to find a job in Ireland? Would Anna marry me? She could have her Catholic life here. I could have my secular life, now that Ireland wasn't so Catholic anymore. Heck, I'd even marry her in the Church, if that's what she wanted.

I see now I was deluding myself. But "love is blind," as the old cliché goes. The two weeks were nearly up. Tomorrow would be our "anniversary": Valentine's Day. I decided to go for broke: propose to Anna. The night before was actually very special. We were completely connected, just like in the old days. Anna even held my hand while we sat before a big, log fire in the farmhouse. She still loved me, I knew it. How could she say no?

# II

## Happy Valentine's Day

THE next morning I woke from a terrible dream. It was another African nightmare. I saw that village again—it was always the same village. People with barely enough to eat. Disease. Misery, palpable misery everywhere. Flies in the heat. Vultures. And then something new came—Boeing B52s appeared in the sky. The village was being bombed by NATO. But the bombs weren't bombs. They were bundled up copies of newspapers and magazines: *The Wall Street Journal*, the *Financial Times* of London and *The Economist*. But when the bundles hit the ground, they detonated just like bombs—destroying everything.

I sat bolt upright, terrified. I realised it was a dream, of course. But I couldn't shake it off. I paced about the room. Then, I stared out the window to a world in white. Overnight, thick snow had fallen everywhere. It was beautiful, magical and it helped to calm me. Then, I remembered what I had in mind to do.

Nervously, I entered the kitchen. Anna was already there making coffee. It's too embarrassing to repeat everything I said. I blathered about honouring each other's different paths. And about our mutual respect for one another, even though we were so different. Then I told her I could see living here, if that's what she wanted.

"Living here?" she said. Obviously, she didn't have a clue what I was driving at.

"In Ireland," I said. Then, I blurted the whole thing out. "Anna, I'm sorry I don't have a ring. But it's our special day today. I know you love me. I love you. I've always loved you. Please marry me."

"Marry?" Anna faltered. "I—I don't know what to say."

"Don't say anything yet. Just think about it. All these years later, all these changes we've been through, yet we still love each

29

other. How many people can say that? This time in Ireland proves it. We haven't grown apart. If anything, we're getting on better than ever. We have some problems, yes, but so does everyone else. But we still love each other. I love you. I never loved anyone like I love you!"

Then, I did something impulsive, crazy. I stepped forward, seized Anna around the waist, pulled her towards me and kissed her. Anna didn't resist. We hadn't kissed for five years. Perhaps there was a heaven, after all. It lasted maybe nine seconds, but it felt like eternity.

Reality intervened. Anna began to resist, gently at first. I persisted. Then she pushed me away, forcefully. "No, no, no," she cried. "This is wrong. Can't you see that?"

Anna fell on her knees on the kitchen floor and started sobbing. "I am so, so sorry I've misled you. Can't you see? We can't ever marry. There's too much standing between us. I am sorry for anything I've done to make you think…"

Anna wailed. All she could say was "I'm sorry, I'm sorry." I was mute, completely mute. Strangled inside. Anna stopped crying and for a few minutes, there was nothing but terrible silence. I stared down at the floor. Anna stared out the window into whiteness.

"I've got to go to Dublin," she said at last.

"What, today?!"

"Yes, I think we need some space. And I didn't tell you. There's this priest I've been wanting to meet there. He thinks there's a chance some traditional French nuns might relocate to Ireland to start a new convent. I need to explore the possibilities…"

Then, she started packing her things and headed towards her car. "I am so sorry," she said, getting in. "I've really let you down. I should never have… Look, I'll be back tonight. We can talk then. I just think some space will do us both good."

And with that she was off.

Happy Valentine's Day.

I walked back to the kitchen and kicked the wastebin over. I'd burnt some porridge the day before and it came splattering out all over the kitchen floor. Then, I broke down and started sobbing myself. How could I be such an idiot?

But was I really an idiot? Wasn't it true what I said: Anna and I had never stopped loving each other? Her crazy religion was the problem, wasn't it? Not us.

Wasn't that right? Or was Anna right? I was totally confused. It was then I found myself doing something utterly incongruous. Sitting with my elbows on the kitchen table, I actually joined my hands together in prayer: "Please, if there is some kind of God up there, please help me find a way. Please help us find a way…"

I didn't know what else to say. I just couldn't bear to lose Anna again to some newly established Irish nuttery. Sorry, nunnery.

I looked out the window. The snow was falling heavily now. One thing was certain: I couldn't sit in this empty farmhouse all day. I would go insane. And I was scared the snow might get too deep to drive down the farm track to the main road.

Mechanically, I got into my rented car and headed down the track and off on the road to Monaghan. But, in the snow, I missed a turning, getting lost on some narrow, old road. I came over the brow of a hill and—just when you'd think nothing else could go wrong—a stupid fox ran out in front of me. I slammed on the brakes and swerved to the right. The car skidded down the hill and slid into a ditch.

Somehow, I hit my head, hard, for I lost consciousness. After a few minutes, I came to. Fortunately, my body seemed intact. I got out of the car. My vision was slightly blurred at first and my head was pulsating. I guess I had a mild concussion.

Cursing, all I could do was tramp back through the snow to look for the main road. Eventually, I found it. A sign said two miles to Monaghan and I started walking. After five minutes, an old woman stopped and offered me a lift into town. I hadn't even tried to hitchhike. But this was Ireland. I couldn't imagine a woman her age stopping for me like that in England.

I don't think she realised I was injured and I didn't tell her. She apologised, said she was in a terrible hurry, but could she drop me off in the high street? She let me out at what looked like the dead centre of the town. It was the dead centre in another way, too. No one was shopping in this miserable weather. The town seemed utterly still. I stood on the pavement as she sped off. My head still throbbed and I was unsure what to do. Should I find a doctor or just sort out the car? It was then that I was given a sign.

It was, quite literally, a sign—hanging above a door, over the street. It was carved in wood and shaped like an old-fashioned pub-sign. But this was no pub-sign. It was, in fact, the strangest sign I'd ever seen. It read:

THE GENTLE
Traditionalist

CLARIFICATIONS PROVIDED
QUESTIONS ANSWERED
ARGUMENTS ASSERTED

*All in the*
*Most Gentle Manner*
*humanly possible*

(**Entirely** *Free of Charge*
**to all** *Genuine Enquirers*)

I don't know how long I stood, staring up at that sign above my head. Everything else on the street looked completely normal. To one side was a barber, the other a bookshop. But between the two, a glass door led to a staircase. Another sign, laminated cardboard this time, was hanging on the glass:

The Gentle Traditionalist is IN
Upstairs on the 3rd floor

(Help also provided with
Romantic Dilemmas)

This was something I had to see. In my dazed condition, I didn't even register how the two signs—taken together—weirdly seemed to fit my current situation. Certainly, I never expected a consultant to help me understand (free of charge) Anna's bizarre traditional outlook—or what to do with my feelings for her. I just had to see what crazy Irish person would hang up a sign like that.

I began climbing the stairs. They were steep and became even steeper as I climbed. They were also narrow and twisting, veering off in odd, unexpected directions. Altogether, it felt like six flights—not three. At last, I found a small landing at the top, with a large, oak door. On it was yet another sign:

---

## ENTER AT YOUR OWN RISK

Life-altering changes probable

(All in the Most Gentle Manner
humanly possible)

---

Curiosity got the better of me. There was no turning back now. I knocked on the door. A loud voice boomed out from within, "Come through!" And through I went.

# III

# The Gentle Traditionalist

I'm not sure what I expected, some sort of office perhaps, like a consultant would have. But it was nothing of the sort. Instead, an open fire blazed away. Above it hung a picture of Jesus pointing to his heart. Beside it on the mantelpiece, a red lamp burnt. Two comfortable chairs were pulled up next to the hearth. In one of them sat a rotund man sporting a slightly faded tweed jacket and trousers. His hair and beard were as white as the snow outside and he looked *ancient*—ninety years or more.

The man rose to greet me. Not only was his girth considerable, but his height, too. He stood well over six feet and was not in the least bent, like many men his age. It was here our dialogue began, and it's easiest if I record it as a dialogue. Like I say, I'm not really a writer. Mainly, I just want to record what GT said to me on that extraordinary Valentine's Day.

> GT: I am Gilbert Tracey—the Gentle Traditionalist. Just call me GT. How can I help you?

> GPL: Well, I'm not quite sure. I can't figure out exactly what it is you do here!

> GT: Oh, a bit of this. A bit of that. Mostly, I try to make tradition intelligible in a divided world. Have a seat...

Hesitantly, I sat down. It felt good to get warm, anyway. My feet were wet through from the snow. Soon, the fire was thawing my frozen toes. GT's accent was striking. It had a soft Irish lilt, but was exceedingly genteel, well-spoken.

> GT: So much misunderstanding these days, you know. My specialty is liberal-conservative conflicts. It's everywhere at the moment. Not just here in Ireland. The culture wars in

America. Red States. Blue States. Families are divided, even lovers or would-be lovers. May I ask your name, good sir?

GPL: Geoffrey Luxworthy...

GT: What is your middle name, please?

GPL: Peter—but that's a bit direct of you. I thought you were meant to be gentle!

GT: I said I was gentle; I didn't say I was polite!

Your initials, then, are GPL. That will suit the purpose of our dialogue most admirably. For I propose it could also stand for Gentle Perplexed Liberal.

Because I sense you are not of a traditionalist nature, yourself. But indeed quite, quite liberal. At the same time, I think you've arrived with genuine questions. You're not here for one of those tiresome battles, where no-one ever listens to each other.

GPL: Yes, yes, you are right, I am also weary of battles, but I am a bit puzzled. Maybe *perplexed* is right.

GT: I appreciate this honest, considerate reply. GPL fits you splendidly. Of course, it might also stand for Gentle Protestant Liberal. I take it you are Protestant—or have Protestant origins, at least?

GPL: Well, my grandfather was devout Church of England. His wife was Quaker, though.

GT: Most English Liberals have roots like that—liberalism does not generally emerge from Catholicism.

GPL: I take it you're Catholic?

GT: Why, yes, of course, who else would put up a sign like that?

GPL: I really have no idea why *anyone* would put up a sign like that! Does anyone ever come here?

GT: Very rarely. And they usually leave quickly.

GPL: Then what on earth is the point of renting this space, hanging out this sign and waiting for days on end...

GT: Weeks usually.

GPL: Then why—?

GT: You are thinking, my friend, strictly in terms of the profit motive, which is neither particularly traditional, nor indeed Catholic. Perhaps I was merely waiting for someone like you to come along.

GPL: Someone like me?

GT: Of course, what we need in this enormous societal upheaval are two people who can discuss things without trying to throttle the other like most liberals and conservatives do.

You, sir, I see are different: genuinely searching. As for myself, I am, if not always polite, then at least genuinely concerned people are neither unnecessarily offended, nor denied clear explanations, if they are honestly perplexed...

Perplexed didn't even come close to how I felt. Who was this wacko—and what was I doing there? Yet as odd as GT was, somehow he put me at ease. A big black cat appeared, nuzzling itself at my legs. Then, it jumped onto GT's lap and started purring, whilst the old man tickled his ears. Through a window behind GT, I could see the snowflakes falling. A sweet fragrance permeated the room. I looked around and saw a censor burning with frankincense. The whole place had a rustic, antique feel. A large crucifix hung on one wall, whilst bookshelves lined another wall with faded volumes. There was also an ancient gramophone with a large horn in one corner and a strange grandfather clock in the other. Instead of twelve numerals, though, it had twelve small faces. I had no idea who the faces were.

What with the sweet smell, the gently falling snow, the purring cat, and the warmth of the fire, there was something deeply comforting, even mesmerising, about the scene. Something else drew my attention, too. GT had enormous, fleshy hands. And on the middle finger of his right hand, he wore a huge ring with a large red stone. It looked like a ruby, but it couldn't have been. It was so big it would have cost a fortune. And everything else about GT, including his well-worn jacket, was comparatively modest. I stared at the fiery red stone.

GPL: That's some ring you have there.

GT: Family heirloom. It's a trifle ostentatious, I admit. Still, I need it in my line of work. My grandfather made it with his own hands—to ward off demons.

At that point, I should have stood up and headed straight for the door. That is, if things were normal. But things were decidedly *not* normal. It was ridiculous, but I felt at ease, even at home, with this loon. I found myself wanting to open up to the big guy.

GPL: It is indeed odd to find you here. In fact, I've been wanting someone to help me understand the exact issues you describe: those which separate modern, liberal people, as you call them, from conservatives. I've met this conservative type—a woman. Really, I cannot understand half the things she's talking about.

GT: Yes—your culture never provided you the means to understand.

GPL: Well, I don't know about that...

GT: You're intelligent, educated—and yet her different views are completely unintelligible to you. There must be a reason. Is it not possible you've been *culturally denied* the keys to understanding? I can help you with that, I think. Who is this lady?

GPL: An old girlfriend. I thought I'd lost her forever. Then, we met again. But now she wants to be a nun!

GT: A nun, huh? That's tough. Well, she may have a vocation—or she may not.

GPL: I still love her... God, I don't believe I'm telling you all this.

GT: I'm not God. Still, I do my best to work for Him. Perhaps you just sense someone gentle you can trust. (Even if, as you may see, I do get a bit crotchety at times. Particularly if I miss Mass.) But please, do tell me more.

I still can't believe what I did then. I guess the pain that morning was too much for me. Anna running off to Dublin, just when I'd been stupid enough to propose to her. Somehow, I could no longer help myself. Everything came pouring out. All these years of loving Anna, all these years of being rejected, first for New Age nuttiness, now this Roman Catholic nuttiness. GT didn't take offense when I said that. No, he listened, carefully, attentively. And he *was* gentle. Really, he was very, very kind to me.

# IV

## Two Opposed Religions?

GT must have listened to me for over an hour. He didn't say much, but when he did, it was always uncannily appropriate, as though he possessed insight not only into my situation, but also into Anna's. It was bizarre how much he apparently understood this person he had never met. All along, he seemed to think Anna and I had something real—that maybe God didn't want her to be a nun.

GPL: You really think there's some kind of hope for Anna and me?

GT: It all depends on consciousness. Your only hope, I think, lies in becoming conscious of certain issues that prefer to remain firmly unconscious. I'll cut to the quick, GPL: your problem with your old girlfriend is that you both have two different religions—only you don't realise it.

GPL: Me? I don't have any religion!

GT: Are you sure?

GPL: Of course, I'm sure!

GT: Then why are you arguing *against* her religion? What are you fighting *for*?

GPL: Well, I can't accept many of her narrow-minded positions.

GT: You put that in the negative. You're fighting *against* something you can't accept. Again, you must be fighting *for* something you believe in—whether you realise it consciously or not.

GPL: Maybe—but that's not the same as having a religion!

GT: Isn't it? It seems to me there's a crisis of consciousness here. It's the same with Western Civilisation. The only hope lies in realising that people—good people, like you and Anna—are separated into two opposed religions. Christianity—and that other one.

GPL: I really have no idea what you're talking about.

GT: I know you don't, GPL! Your liberal culture has done everything it can to conceal the real issues here. Hmm… I wish I could illustrate it for you. Well, let's see now, how shall we do that? I know, I have an idea…

At that moment, AL—his initials, of course—shot through the door. He looked like a wild man with long hair in a pigtail, wearing torn jeans and a *Grateful Dead* T-shirt.

GT: Ah, my good man, what can I do for you?

AL: Don't "my good man" me, you crazy old coot! You can call me Al. Who is this here? Another one of your suckers?

GT: Why no, indeed. This is my friend Geoffrey and (although I don't think Geoffrey realises it yet) you and he share the same religion. Geoffrey, meet Alberto Lasagne— or AL as I tend to call him.

AL: He calls me Angry Liberal!

GT: Well, forgive me, but the term will help us clarify things for our purposes here. And you do seem rather liberal to me. And certainly a trifle agitated. Dare I say *angry*…?

AL: Damn right, I'm angry! And Genghis Khan would look like a liberal next to you!

Don't listen to this guy, Geoffrey. He appears all calm and nice, on the surface. But you'll soon find out he's a rabid, frothing at the mouth, misogynist, homophobic, reactionary fascist!

GPL: Misogynist, ho—?

AL: What about all those anti-woman positions you have? What about your Church's ban on women priests? Tell Geoffrey about that!

GT: The only way I could positively discriminate against women being priests is if women possessed a right—an automatic right—to be priests.

AL: What are you talking about?! Of course, women have the right to be priests. Women have rights to be or do anything they want!

GT: Like a right to abort their children.

AL: Yes, of course, women have a right to choose— although a foetus is a foetus. Not a child.

GT: That is rather convenient, isn't it? Otherwise, we would be talking about murder.

AL: Oh God!

GT: Like I said to Geoffrey, I'm not God. I only work for Him. (And the Good Lord knows, I fail him miserably.)

Anyway, we appear have several *beliefs* here: Women have a right to ordination; a foetus is not a child; abortion isn't murder. I think we will uncover more beliefs if we proceed. For example, homosexuals have a right to marry and raise children...

AL: Exactly, you homophobe! This is not the Middle Ages! We've gone beyond all your backward prejudices now.

GT: This "going beyond"... I am "backward." You *believe* that what I *believe* is mere prejudice. And *nothing* else. My belief is wrong according to your belief. Oh, there are many, many beliefs here—if one only digs a little deeper.

Moreover, there's something else here than just beliefs. We have a grouping—*a collective distinctly identified as "we."* "*We've* gone beyond." Who is this "we," I wonder? You talk to me as though I *should* belong to your collective.

AL: This is the twenty-first century, you dinosaur!

GT: Yes, precisely, I am being commandeered to join the religion of the twenty-first century. Otherwise, I risk being condemned of heresy...

AL: What the f—...

But before he could finish the sentence, GT had reached down for something by the side of his chair. It was a small pail of water with a metal implement. Picking the dripping implement up, he used it to swiftly scatter drops of water over AL.

AL: You're throwing water at me?! How old are you—three?

GT: Just a little Holy Water. Won't harm you a bit. Quite the opposite, in fact.

AL: I give up! You're nuts! You're a crazy old coot, do you know that?!

Al Lasagne stood there rigid, eyes bulging, face turning crimson. If he didn't have a pigtail, I swear his hair might have stood on end. For a moment, I thought he might lunge for GT, but, instead, he turned around abruptly and stormed out of the room, slamming the door.

GT: I always keep some Holy Water handy for times like this. It does have its uses, you know. Our ancestors knew that perfectly well.

Still, that should be enough to illustrate my point. Although I fear I wasn't gentle enough with the good fellow. *Mea culpa. Mea maxima culpa.* Anyway, you get my drift, GPL.

There really is a *"we"* here.

That *"we"* holds *multiple beliefs* about the nature of existence. Whether a foetus is a child or not is only the tip of the iceberg. Those beliefs carry with them *ethical imperatives*: Thou shalt give a woman a "right" to abort, for example. Or thou shalt ordain women priests.

Moreover, this "we" tells me I ought to subscribe to its beliefs. And it condemns people when they don't—even pronounces their beliefs "anathema."

GPL: His beliefs seem pretty reasonable to me.

GT: Well, yes, of course, they would *to you*. You share his beliefs, don't you?

GPL: Well, yes—most people do these days.

GT: *Most* people—are you sure? I have a few hundred million friends in Africa who don't agree. Also Saudi Arabia, India, not to mention Russia. To say nothing of millions of my practicing Catholic friends in Europe and the Americas. Nor my Protestant friends in the Bible belt...

But we all know the rest of humanity is "backward," don't we? Those rednecks just haven't caught up with us advanced liberals in the Anglosphere. We're the ones who hold "the way, the truth and the life" now.

GPL: You're being sarcastic.

GT: Yes, forgive me. It is a sin, to be sure. *Mea culpa. Mea culpa. Mea maxima culpa.* I confess I find it very trying, sometimes.

GPL: Well, I confess, your point is taken, GT. The majority opinion in England is not the entire universe. I guess I forget that sometimes.

GT: Thank you, GPL. I could tell you were a gentle person from the start. Probably much more gentle than me. *Mea culpa.*

And, indeed, that is my point—your liberal worldview is far from universal. It's largely concentrated in the educated classes of America and Europe, mainly the old Protestant Europe in fact—England, Holland, Sweden, etc. Much less so in Poland, Greece or Spain! When you boil it down, it's a sliver of humanity.

Alas, this small sliver is not restricted to the educational elites. It also dominates the main opinion-making bodies these days. You know: the trendsetters, TV, radio—Hollywood. People like me don't get much airtime. Or if we do, we're deliberately set up to be laughed at.

Forgive me, GPL, but I am not sure that—even in hyperliberal England—"most" people genuinely, deeply share your liberal beliefs or whether they've just been cowed into submission by these powerful elites. They are, at very least, highly influenced by those who control the media.

GPL: Well, nobody denies the power of the media.

GT: Let's come back to the media later. My real point is that relatively few people are truly committed to these values. Unqualified acceptance of these things is restricted to the elites in a small number of countries. It's all quite, quite provincial, when you examine it closely. It's also provincial in time...

GPL: Provincial in time?

GT: Yes, if you think about it, many of these beliefs only go back to the 1960s. Admittedly, some of them go back as far as 1789—the French Revolution. Of course, the French Revolution was rooted in the Eighteenth Century Enlightenment—the so-called "Age of Reason." But even the Eighteenth Century isn't that long ago. At any rate, what the New Secular Religion believes is relatively recent.

GPL: The New Secular Religion?!

GT: We have to call it *something*. Indulge me—let me call it that for now.

Like I said: we're considering a select group of people with specific beliefs about the nature of reality and ethics—what should or shouldn't be done. But this is just the beginning. We're only getting started. If you give me the gift of your patience, you may see why I call it that.

GPL: Okay, I'll try to be patient...

GT: Splendid, my good man. Anyway, as I was saying, the New Secular Religion has its roots in the Eighteenth Century, to be sure. But in many ways, it only goes back to the 1960s. Before then, people didn't believe many of the things they believe today. For example, that women possess a right to abort their children.

That's why I say "provincial in time"—as well as space. What we're talking about isn't just that elite sliver of humanity in a few Western countries, it's also a sliver of humanity in time. Approximately 1960 till now, if you like. And this sliver of people in time apparently believes that everything after 1960 is self-evidently superior to everything that came before.

**GPL:** Oh, come on now. That can't be right!

**GT:** Well, the 1960s are just a handy approximation. Although some people are even more specific than that. They identify 1968 as the turning point. But think about what I'm saying: *Wherever previous generations disagree with the post-1960s worldview*—let's call it that for short—*previous generations are always wrong.* Post-'60s is always right. At least, according to modern media and education.

Post-'60s says a woman has a so-called "right to choose." Post-'60s must be right; everyone who felt differently, before the '60s, is obviously wrong.

Or take freedom of speech. Only the other day, someone told me pornography was "the price we have to pay" for free speech. All kinds of people say that—*now*. Nobody ever said that *before* the '60s. Westerners believed in freedom of speech in 1950, too. Still, they banned things like *Lady Chatterley's Lover* by D.H. Lawrence. *Literature* was prohibited—to say nothing of pornography. But according to the post-'60s worldview, freedom of speech means pornography should be allowed everywhere. Why didn't people ever think that before the '60s? Why is it only *now* we believe that free speech necessarily includes exhibiting intimate sex acts or sexual perversities or gore? Because almost no one before the 1960s thought something like *Deep Throat* was legitimate under Freedom of Speech. *Deep Throat*—or *The Texas Chainsaw Massacre* for that matter—only became possible in the 1960s.

If you belong to the New Secular Religion, the 1960s revelation is your creed, your Bible. Every generation of people before you, who believed differently, was wrong.

In other words: wherever pre-'60s beliefs *differ* from post-'60s ones, post-'60s is always, always right.

I wasn't sure what to say. I could see where he was going with this and it made me uncomfortable. GT said nothing for some minutes—maybe allowing his point to sink in. I fidgeted in my chair, looking up at his strange grandfather clock with the twelve faces. Finally, I asked him about it.

GPL: That weird clock of yours, with the faces—who are they?

GT: Oh, they're popes! The Pius popes to be precise. There were twelve of them, you know. I thought it made sense to have the whole series—Popes Pius I through Pius XII.

Clearly, what "made sense" in GT's corner of the galaxy versus my corner were two entirely different things. I indicated as much to him.

GT: Yes, two different corners of the galaxy. With two different outlooks—or religions, like I say. Your religion is rooted to a large extent in the 1960s. That's another reason for my clock. It reminds people of history—what happened prior to the '60s.

GPL: A lot of good things happened in the '60s, too. Martin Luther King in America, civil rights, breaking down prejudice, bigotry, hypocrisy…

GT: I won't disagree with you there, GPL. That point seems entirely valid to me. But if you don't mind, I'll return to it later. Right now, if you'll bear with me, my point is how this provincial post-'60s collectivity always regards its revelation as better than anybody else's…

GPL: As a traditional Catholic, you surely think your revelation is the same!

GT: I most certainly do! And that is my point: I belong to a religion too, just like you. My sole point—right now—is that we all have a religion, whether we realise it or not. *We all have multiple beliefs*—conscious or not—*about the nature of existence and what kind of morals flow from it.*

Moreover, we *share those beliefs with like-minded others.* You share a great deal with my friend AL—even if you are much more gentle. I share a religion with Anna.

We have two groupings here, two distinct tribes or collectivities. Your Anna and I belong to one tribe. You belong to another tribe, which many post-'60s English people do. Even if pre-'60s English people didn't and most other people on the planet still don't.

GPL: I see what you're driving at. But I still don't think I'm a practising member of a religion, simply because I believe in a few basic human rights.

GT: Once again: what your tribe *believes* to be a right. But perhaps you mean there's a difference because my religion has many beliefs, whilst you have limited beliefs in a few basic things like rights.

GPL: Something like that.

GT: Well, I wouldn't be too sure. Dig deeper. You'll find far more implicit belief in today's secular creed, if you care to look. Also ethical commandments. "Thou shalt use inclusive language." "Thou shalt be politically correct." "Thou shalt not tip thy hat at the ladies and open doors for them." "Thou shalt not smoke." "Thou shalt not dare question liberal orthodoxy or, if thou dost, thou shalt stand condemned as an antediluvian monster."

GPL: Okay, okay, sometimes I get worried all this political correctness is getting tyrannical. Let's say I even agree with you—that there is some secular belief-system with its own moral imperatives—that still isn't a religion. Religions are about God—stuff like that.

GT: Are they? A Buddhist will tell you his religion is not about God. Some will tell you Buddhism is mainly just dharma—a "right way of living," they might say. Is secularism that different?

GPL: All right, Buddhists may not believe in God, but they still believe in something. Nirvana, maybe.

GT: Yes, they still believe in something. They have *a metaphysical order from which their moral imperatives flow.* Is that what you mean by religion?

GPL: Yeah, maybe—I'm no philosopher, but a metaphysical order as the basis of ethics sounds about right to me.

GT: Secularism has the same—at least implicitly.

GPL: You're losing me...

GT: Tell me, what do you think of euthanasia?

GPL: Well, if someone is in horrible, horrible pain and they want to end it, they should have the right to do that, shouldn't they?

GT: Let's say they do. They don't only do that, do they?

GPL: I'm not sure what you mean...?

GT: Well, for one, they set an example to others. Granddad had assisted suicide, so did my uncle. Now Auntie Maisie wants it. Everyone's doing it.

GPL: You're saying it's not just a private act. It has public consequences?

GT: That's right.

GPL: Well, okay, maybe we need to set a public example—if it will liberate people from their suffering.

GT: How do you know they're liberated from suffering?

GPL: Isn't it obvious? Do you realise how much some people have to suffer before they die?

GT: Obviously, there is terrible, terrible suffering. Moreover, that's been obvious for thousands of years. You might ask yourself why it is *only now*, after all these centuries, that people try to justify assisted suicide... At any rate, I don't know how I'd face a situation like that myself—especially without the Holy Sacraments. Still, there's a *hidden presumption* operating here. You're assuming the suffering *ends* with the death of the body. You're also assuming suicide isn't a sin which carries consequences in the afterlife.

GPL: Well, yes.

GT: *What if that's not true?* What if the person committing suicide suffers *more* after he dies, than he did before?

GPL: You mean in their soul? Well, that's a religious belief.

GT: Forgive me, my good man, but you just indicated your own religious belief: that the person committing suicide suffers less.

GPL: A religious belief?

GT: You are making implicit statements about the afterlife. For example, that the amount of suffering that exists beyond death must necessarily be less than the suffering in this life. Or that committing suicide carries little or no consequence in the afterlife. You can't make the *equation* you just did— i.e., less suffering versus more suffering—without belief! Moreover, you indicated a wish to *disseminate* your belief— by hoping people might set public examples of your belief-system...

GT lifted a finger. "We have, first: a *belief* about the ultimate nature of reality." Raising another finger, he said, "Second: an *imperative*—this is what people *ought to do* on the basis of that belief." Lifting a final finger, he added, "Third: *public demonstration* of your 'path of liberation from suffering.' That looks awfully like religion to me."

At that point, I simply did not know what to say to the old man.

GT: That's what I meant by secularism possessing its own implicit metaphysics. The secular notion of a right to suicide is based on the tacit belief in the here and now. We calculate how much suffering does or doesn't exist by what we see in this physical world.

In other words: *Only the material world counts in the New Secular Religion.* Either no other world exists or it if it does, it doesn't matter. It counts for nothing. You have a materialist metaphysic—either *de jure* or *de facto*...

You see what I am driving at. Here we have an "ethic"— an alleged right to suicide—which then pioneers an entire culture of suicide. And all of this is implicitly based on a presumed metaphysical order.

It's the same with all religions. Buddhists don't believe in God. Inevitably, that helps form their ethics. Christians do believe in God—a personal God—and their ethics are formed by that. Secular Materialists don't believe in an afterlife and that, likewise, shapes their ethics.

We both fell silent. I stared out the window into snow. The hand of the clock pointed to Pius XI.

GPL: This is getting heavy. I need to do some homework.

GT: We all do, my friend. It's the only way to combat the media manipulating our minds. Another obvious example is abortion. Christians believe a child is a child from the moment of conception. Today's secular religionists don't. Out of that metaphysic flows...

GPL: If I'm honest, I'm confused, but I do get your point: there is a secular system of belief, based on—what did you call it—a presumed metaphysical order?

GT: Yes, we always have a metaphysic—whether we like it or not. That metaphysic leads to law. The secular metaphysic has many rules. All those politically correct *shalt* and *shalt nots* we mentioned earlier. It goes much further than this—but we don't have all day.

Still, if I may remind you, all this entails a distinct collectivity of people. Some of us belong to that secular tribe. Some of us don't. Those of us who don't—like myself—are treated like heretics because we don't believe...

GPL: I begin to see why you call it a religion. I need to do some thinking here.

GT: Yes, please go and think, really think, for yourself. But permit me to make one last proposition here: All this entails a monstrous double standard. *Because secularism pretends to be neutral, it gets away with murder.*

In other words: one belief-system—secularism—is privileged in our society simply because it denies being a belief-system! If secularism ever owned-up to what it actually is— a belief-system with its own metaphysic, its own ethics, its own disciples and its own heretics—the game would be over! Secularism would just be another creed among others without any special privileges attached to it.

Our education and media are profoundly invested in that not happening. A materialist metaphysic and ethic is privileged in our schools, our universities, our television, our press—everything. Not just privileged—*powerfully reinforced.* Every day, round the clock. It's become such a "normal" part of our existence, no-one seems to notice anymore!

**GPL:** Whoa!

**GT:** Like I say: That's a proposition for you to consider. Still, whether you agree with me or not, it's pertinent, I think, to the intimate matters you entrusted with me.

**GPL:** With Anna, you mean?

**GT:** Precisely. You and she participate in a conflict far greater than yourselves. It's a global conflict, I'd say. And it doesn't matter what terms you use: liberal versus conservative, secular versus traditional, etc., etc. It forms the crisis of our age. Men and women everywhere are embroiled in its ramifications. But it's problematic if one isn't aware of the fact. Becoming conscious, however, will help you find peace with Anna.

**GPL:** She is... I have to say... often not as clear-thinking as you. Sometimes, she just gets angry when I don't agree...

**GT:** And you get angry when she doesn't?

**GPL:** Sometimes, yes, I admit.

**GT:** Voilà! That's the real problem here, my friend. As Hilaire Belloc was fond of quoting: "All human conflict is ultimately theological."

**GPL:** Belloc—didn't he write children's books?

**GT:** Oh, *much* more than that. Old friend of mine from the trenches. I can say more, another time. Right now, I propose that resolving things with your old love demands understanding her religion—not necessarily accepting it—but understanding how and why it differs from your own metaphysical system of belief.

**GPL:** I can see how you could help me with that.

**GT:** I didn't hang that sign on the door for any other reason...

# V

## Bee Nice

SITTING cosily beside the fire, my feet were now warmed through and dry. Outside the window, little flakes of snow drifted down. I felt extraordinarily comfortable. A distinct peace filled the room. I told myself it was simply the fire, the gently falling snow. Nothing else. Snow always does that.

But, to be honest, I knew there was more. Not only had GT comforted me after the dreadful morning with Anna, but I began to feel this strange, inexplicable hope in Anna and me. It made me soften to GT. I wanted to argue with the old man's ridiculous notions of my so-called "secular creed." But I decided to let it slide, at least for the moment.

> **GT**: The thing is, Anna already understands your religion. Unless she was raised in very sheltered conditions, she's been plugged into it from the moment she was born. The New Secular Religion's all over the airwaves, radio, TV, now internet. By contrast, you hardly understand anything about her religion. Am I right?

> **GPL**: I'm afraid you're right. I mean I get some basic things. Obviously, I know what she means by God, I think. I get the nature of the soul— something that continues after death. I don't disagree with any of that. There must be something more to the universe than just this...

> **GT**: Material world?

> **GPL**: Yes.

> **GT**: Even a benevolent something?

> **GPL**: Yeah, I think so. No, I'm sure of it.

GT: Well, that's a start: a benevolent, non-materialist meta-physic. Perhaps you are closer to Anna than you think. Still, there's plenty you don't understand—or accept.

GPL: Yes, yes—Jesus Christ died for my sins. MY sins—two thousand years later. What's that supposed to mean? And all these rules and regulations...

It was easier before, when she was a New Ager. She just had a few basic concepts then. We had a soul. That soul was growing or evolving. There was some kind of universal force—I could see that. Back then, she said the only thing that really mattered was being a good person...

That's what I liked about the New Age thing. It didn't make so many demands. I could handle that better than "Hail Mary, pray for us sinners" and all this dogma.

GT: Sometimes I call that *minimum commitment spirituality.*

GPL: Yes. Seems like a good strategy to me. Just find some basic core ideas everyone can agree on and forget the rest. Why can't we just agree to disagree? She was more open-minded when she was a New Ager. She believed in some sort of universal religion back then. It seemed less narrow, if you ask me.

GT: Less narrow and more vague perhaps?

GPL: Perhaps. But also less divisive. More accepting of dif-ferences. Now, she's got all these sectarian doctrines.

At that point, someone rapped on the door. GT opened it and a tall, lanky man wearing an orange tie-dyed kaftan stepped into the room. He had a mellow American accent, which I couldn't quite place. West Coast, I thought, maybe Californian.

"Welcome, welcome," GT said cheerily. "I am Gilbert Tracey—the Gentle Traditionalist. And what might your name be?"

The visitor apparently didn't like the question. "Me? I don't have a name," he said. "It's better that way. People get too hung up on naming things. Pretty soon, we're all divided from each other."

"Well, I have to call you something. Can I call you No Name for now?"

"Hey, yeah, that's cool," No Name smiled. "I like that. If only everyone had no name! There'd be no more wars and killing and religion and stuff like that!"

"Where are you from, No Name?"

"Same place as you're from—the Universe!" Slowly, a broad, toothy grin fanned out across No Name's face, as though he had just said something enormously profound and satisfying.

"Could you be a bit more specific, please?" GT prodded.

"But why?" No Name didn't like this. "We're all the same, man. I am you. You are me. We're, like, all together. Goo goo goo joob, you know? Nothing to get hung about."

"*I am the Walrus, Strawberry Fields Forever,*" I said, recognising the Beatles' references.

No Name: Yeah, man, exactly! The universe is just an infinite strawberry patch! If you start identifying with different places, everyone gets separated. You get wars, nationalism, religious hatred—stuff like that. We are all children of the same Universe!

GT: You can't post a letter to the universe.

No Name: You're right. What a drag. Still, we won't need post offices in the future. We'll all just be able to tune in to each other.

GT: Telepathically, you mean? How do you know that?

No Name: Well, everyone says that.

GT: Who is everyone?

No Name: Well, you know everyone who's really spiritually conscious I guess. All the great masters and spiritual teachers.

GT: Like St John of the Cross, I suppose, or St Teresa of Avila?

No Name: Who are they? I never heard of them.

GT: They're great Catholic saints.

**No Name**: Oh, Catholic! That's so, you know, um… medieval—Old Age and rigid. No, I mean like Deepak Chopra or Neale Donald Walsch: teachers of higher consciousness.

**GT**: Ah yes, the masters. And Sri Baba Rama Ding-Dong?

**No Name**: Yeah, yeah! That's what I mean—teachers like that!

**GT**: What about Jesus?

**No Name**: Well, Jesus was cool! It's just the Church messed up everything he said.

**GT**: How do you know that?

**No Name**: Well, you know, everyone knows that now. There was this guy Dan Brown who found out Jesus and Mary Magdalene were lovers. Everyone knows that.

**GT**: Everyone who's really spiritually conscious, you mean.

**No Name**: Well, yeah.

**GT**: What about the Pope?

**No Name**: Oh, he's not spiritually conscious! Everyone knows that. Well, maybe this new Pope Francis is a little bit conscious. He's kinda cool. But before him, they were all like, you know, totally unconscious. Hey, are you a Catholic or something?

**GT**: I am.

**No Name**: Oh, sorry dude. I didn't mean to rag on your religion like that. Your religion's cool, too.

**GT**: Why, thank you, my good man. I will endeavour to take whatever consolation I can from that!

**No Name**: It's just like every spiritual path. They all lead to the same place in the end, right?

**GT**: Well, if, by that, you mean merging with the universe, where no names, no separation, no division exists, I would have to say no.

**No Name**: Man, that's the problem with you Christians! You all think you're going somewhere different from the rest of us. You're all so judgmental and arrogant. Like you've got to do it my way or else!

With that, a plump, plain little woman timidly popped her head through the door. She had a Dutch accent and black hair and wore a golden-orange sweater with black stripes. And she seemed positively taken with No Name. GT welcomed her in. She explained in a flustered voice, "I'm sorry, I've been listening to this conversation from the top of the stairs. I'm afraid I really have to agree with No Name. I don't mean to be negative about Christianity, but, frankly, sometimes it isn't very nice. Religion ought to be nice—not something that scares people with all this judgement stuff."

"And your name is...?" GT asked.

"Bernice. But people just call me Bee."

Suddenly, No Name looked like he'd had a revelation: "Hey, you know what happens if you take the 'r' out of Bernice? You get Be nice. Geddit?"

"Hey, that's like, totally amazing! I never thought of that before, No Name! I'll Bee Nice from now on!" She giggled and No Name looked like he'd just scored a goal.

**Bee Nice:** It's a good philosophy to live by. Be nice. Don't scare people.

**GT:** Not scaring people is important. *Essentially,* your aspiration is gentleness. I salute that.

**Bee Nice:** That's important, isn't it? The thing is, if you tell someone they've done all these bad things, they're not going to feel good, are they? I mean, if you tell me I've done bad, then I feel bad.

**No Name:** Right on, man.

**GT:** But what if you *have* done bad?

**Bee Nice:** Why do you have to call it "bad"? Again, you're scaring me with language like that. I try to use "'I' statements"—like "I feel scared" or "I feel upset." For example: "I feel scared when people talk about people being bad." You see, I just named my emotions. That's all I did: Nothing more. If everyone used "'I' statements" like that, there'd be no need to judge people.

GT: Well, again, your essential intention is gentleness. I see that. No doubt these "'I' statements" have real value at times. However, we can't spend our entire life in subjectivism. What would you say about Hitler?

Bee Nice: Well, I feel sad about what Hitler did. He came from a terribly deprived background, didn't he? Maybe he grew up scared of being judged.

GT: That isn't my point. Objectively speaking, were Hitler's concentration camps good or bad?

Bee Nice: Well, I prefer not to be judgmental. I just want to make "'I' statements."

No Name: Cool. Her karma just ran over your dogma, dude!

GT: Indeed, I am not sure there is any ground for conversation if all we can make are "'I' statements."

No Name: Hey, you just made an "'I' statement"! You're catching on!

At that point, I was unable to resist interjecting.

GPL: I'm afraid you're both missing the point here. What GT means is that if everything is reduced simply to one's purely subjective emotions, there's no possibility of any common evaluation—or objective perspective. Everything becomes completely solipsistic.

No Name: Uh, yeah, right. Whatever, dude. Anyway, I've got to be going. This is getting too heavy for me.

Bee Nice: I must be going, too.

GT: All right, my friends. But do you mind if I sprinkle you with Holy Water before you go? Just an old form of blessing I like to administer when anyone takes their leave.

No Name: Uh... sure, okay.

Bee Nice: Why not?

GT scattered his Holy Water over the two of them. I couldn't help but notice their faces soften a little. Bee Nice, who had been looking wistfully at No Name from the start, now beamed at him. Indeed, she looked positively smitten.

No Name obviously noticed her attention. "Hey, Bee Nice, can I buy you lunch somewhere?" he asked. "I know this little veggie place just north of Belfast... I mean, it's two hours from here. But it's really great."

"That would be so lovely, No Name. Thank you."

"North? Belfast? Why, No Name, you surprise me," GT said with a twinkle in his eye. "That sounds awfully specific, coming from you. Are you sure you want to limit yourself like that?"

"You know what, old man? You're absolutely right!" No Name was getting excited now. His fist pumped the air. "We were born—born to be free! No limitations! No directions! C'mon babe, let's hit the highway! We're taking the road to nowhere!"

"That sounds totally awesome, No Name." By now, she looked completely gooey-eyed.

"Yes, go, my children," GT smiled. "Be fruitful and multiply. And don't forget me on your big day. Pity it can't be a nuptial Mass..."

"Nuptial what?" No Name looked momentarily confused. "Whatever, dude—anything for peace, love, and understanding!"

Shaking the old man's hand, he opened the door for Bee Nice with a mock-gallant gesture. And off they went, hand in hand.

GT: Nice kids, really. They'll need looking out for, though. Anyway, where were we?

GPL: I believe you were talking about minimum commitment spirituality and I was talking about Anna... again.

GT: Can't stop thinking about her, can you?

GPL: Not really. Anyway, meeting those two has reminded me of how Anna used to be. Maybe being Catholic is an improvement, after all. She seems less flighty these days, at any rate.

GT: More committed?

I didn't want to admit it, but I took his point. Anna appeared more defined now; she had edges. Sometimes in the past, she seemed so spaced-out, you could pass your hand straight through her.

GPL: You're right. She stands for something definite these days. I can see that now. Before everything was kind of…

GT: Fuzzy and all the over the place?

GPL: Well, yeah, maybe that's right.

GT: Chesterton said when you lose faith, you don't believe in "nothing," you end up believing in "anything."

GPL: Chesterton?

GT: Another old friend from the trenches. Along with Belloc. Still, it's not quite as simple as Chesterton said. These young people want to believe in as little as possible: no names, no nationality, no religion…

GPL: No objective reality…

GT: Right. Yet they don't end up in believing in just anything. In fact, they believe *whatever it most pleases them to believe*. And only that: what's nice, pleasant, facile. Avoiding the tough stuff of reality.

That's the problem with minimum commitment spirituality. It sounds good on paper. More tolerant and openminded. But also more empty-headed… vacuous.

Alas, people who don't bother to think become unwitting stooges of the media. Clearly, No Name knew nothing about the Papacy. Apart from what his masters told him. O poor, poor, poor dupes of the global elites!

GPL: That's a bit scathing, isn't it? Aren't you meant to be gentle?

GT: Sometimes one has to call a spade a spade. It's appalling, all these people simply parroting whatever the media tells them. And the global capitalists behind the media, of course. Poor, poor, poor humanity!

Anyway, I said I was gentle; I didn't say I was nice!

GPL: What on earth is the difference?

GT: Oh, being nice—that's easy. Any old fool can be nice! Being gentle is something else. That's where things get tough.

Being nice—these days it usually means denial: what those two were doing. Denying any differences exist between people. We're all children of the same universal goo. Even denying Good and Evil exist.

Being gentle is another thing altogether. It means actively confronting the enormous problem of human differences. Also confronting evil—including the evil that blackens your own heart. And, after you've struggled with all that, still finding a way to honour people's dignity, even if what you'd really like to do is give them a boot up the backside.

In short, being nice inevitably means being easy and simplistic. Being gentle means civilising yourself—taming your own lust to dominate others.

GPL: Why didn't you tell them that?

GT: One must be gentle. You can't force on people what they're not ready to hear. Alas, in our own heart of hearts, that's usually what we want to do. Like I say: dominate people. True gentleness means facing our lust for power.

GPL: That's a pretty grim picture of humanity you have there.

GT: Well, I'm a Christian. I believe the human situation *is* grim. Christ wouldn't have come otherwise.

Unfortunately, a lot of Christians today don't even see that. They've all been swept up in this religion of nice. They try to make Jesus nice. Jesus could be infinitely gentle—but he wasn't nice. Not in this modern way, anyway.

Same with the Popes, like St. John Paul II and Benedict XVI. They weren't nice and bland and fuzzy. They stood for something—strong and clear. They stood strong, because they loved humanity. But the world, the media hated them for that.

He let out a long sigh.

GT: It is very hard. One must pray. Sometimes I say a little prayer in these situations. God help me to be gentle. But God preserve me from being nice!

GPL: That's all very well—but those people weren't completely wrong. They did have some legitimate points, I think. Christianity *has* scared people terribly. The Inquisition is just the beginning...

GT: You are right. We are all guilty. *Nostra culpa. Nostra maxima culpa.*

The old bloke looked tremendously pained when he said this. Stricken to the core, like he'd aged another hundred years. For a few moments, he stared at the floor. Then he lifted his head and said, "Your point is important and must be addressed. I promise you most solemnly: It will be. But could you indulge me again— by waiting a little? It will be easier, I think, after we get to the Heart of the Matter."

"And what's that?"

"Why, some way to bridge you and Anna, of course. Isn't that what you were praying for this morning, before you came?"

I was too stunned to utter a word. At any rate, I was happy to indulge him. If he wanted to address the question of Christian atrocities later, that was fine by me. First, I needed to know what he meant by a "bridge" for Anna and me.

# VI

## The Heart of the Matter

MY mind raced with questions. Who was this enigma sitting before me? Where was he getting all this stuff? What did he mean by a "bridge" for Anna and me? But for long moments, the enigma sat silently in his chair, motionless like the Sphinx.

After some while, the Sphinx started speaking, slowly, carefully. "There are different ways to build a bridge. I think it best if we proceed slowly. Let me begin with a question. Tell me, what do you think of the state of the world?"

The nightmare about Africa I had that morning came back vividly. And suddenly, it all poured out—my whole anti-capitalist spiel. I talked about the IMF and the intolerable debt burden placed on developing countries, whilst we in the West exploited their misery and lived our rich lifestyles. And I talked about the bombs in my dream, which, it seemed to me, represented the smug financial elites who were oh-so-sure that ruthless economic liberalism must be imposed on everyone. And I talked about the environment which can no longer bear the toll of consumer capitalism. To my surprise, GT not only listened intently, but shuddered as I spoke.

"*The Economist*," I raged, "that magazine is a crime against humanity."

"I know, I know," was all GT said, his face ashen.

This I didn't expect from a conservative, Christian fundamentalist. I was even more surprised when he started talking himself. Everything in modern culture was prostituted to the economy, GT said. And he compared the situation to the past, which, while bad, he claimed, was not as dire as today—with global corporations running the world rather than democratically elected governments. People were duped, he said, by the most powerful propaganda ever deployed. But he also counted other casualties of capitalism—not so often heard in left-wing discourse—such as decaying cultural standards and rising mental illness.

I confessed to ignorance about the latter, although my sister, I told him, had a terrible time with her kids. They seem very disturbed, I said. He nodded, adding that the growth curve of mental illness was horrendous. All this he linked to capitalism with its consumer junk culture, rising stress, and wage slavery demanding that both parents work outside the home. I have to say I was impressed. It was also startling how contemporary GT was. Usually, people of his generation seem stuck in the past. But GT even seemed to know pop music.

GPL: There's an old line from that Happy Christmas song by John Lennon. It's only five words long—but it pretty much sums it up for me.

GT: "The world is so wrong."

GPL: Yes, exactly…

Suddenly, he looked afflicted again. "What's the matter?" I asked.

GT: I was thinking of Verdun in World War One. There were 60,000 casualties on the first day alone—as machine guns tore into the British troops trying to cross No Man's Land. Over a million were killed or wounded by the time the battle ended. All for hardly any gain in territory. In the end, the British gained less than one square foot of ground for every casualty…

GPL: Yes, that's it. I mean, we're insane as a species. What kind of sane creature wages war like that—or spends billions of dollars building ICBMs—nuclear warheads, for God's sake!?

GT: It is surely not for God's sake. Maybe the other one…?

GPL: You mean evil again—the devil? Well, I wouldn't go that far. But certainly there's some kind of twisted sickness in the world. That's for sure. Yeah, call it evil, if you like.

GT: So you don't believe in the devil, but you can accept the reality of evil?

GPL: Yes.

GT: Which presupposes you accept the nature of good?

GPL: Evidently.

GT: I'll say it again: your metaphysic may be nearer Anna's than you think.

GPL: Okay, okay. Suppose I admit good and evil exist in the universe. Maybe those are built into the fabric of existence, as it were. I won't deny that. The thing about Christianity is that it's all so *personal*. It's not just good and evil—there's the devil with his horns and pitchfork. And God is a person: an old man who turns into a baby...

GT: I thought you told me *Howard's End* was your favourite novel.

GPL: I never told you that!

GT: Well, not today at any rate. Maybe it was some other time. At King's, maybe...?

This was bewildering. Had I met GT before? It was true I had gone to King's—E. M. Forster's old college at Cambridge. Had I somehow run into the old fellow, back there? But all I could say was, "What on earth has *Howard's End* got to do with any of this?"

GT: "Personal relations are the real life"—isn't that Forster's point in the novel?

GPL: Well, yes. But how is that relevant here?

GT: I would say there's a small, secular glimmer of Christianity, there. God agrees with Forster. He enters into personal relations with us by becoming fully personal...

There's Goethe too: *Das höchste Gut der Erdenkinder ist doch die Persönlichkeit*—"The highest treasure of the children of earth is surely the personality."

GPL: That's beautiful—but so what? Purely secular people say the same thing.

GT: Certainly, all these things exist in the earthly realm, too: good, evil, the human personality.

The point to Christianity is that they're not *limited* to the earthly realm. Not only do good and evil have a transcendent origin—but *personality does too.* Human personality is so utterly beautiful it must come from God.

What Forster calls "personal relations" also comes from God. Not only is God Himself a Trinity—three persons in relationship—but God created humanity in His own image and likeness.

Each human being is a free, independent, creative agent. In other words: individual and personal, like God. That means we humans have the capacity for relationship—with all the personal joy and all the personal suffering relationship entails. That is to say: real relationship between real beings. That's Christianity in a nutshell.

My mind was beginning to reel. For me, this had always been a stumbling block to Christianity. This notion of a personal God. But I began to see I couldn't have my cake and eat it. I'd already admitted to GT I thought there was some kind of higher force, even higher good in the universe. But if you believe that, it doesn't make sense to think that force is impersonal. Not if you also believe in "personal relations."

Because GT was right about E. M. Forster and me—even though I hadn't read *Howard's End* for years, since I was at King's. Anna and I read it together, lazing on the Backs, during an unusually warm September. (The Backs, just in case you don't know, are the famous university gardens that "back" out onto the River Cam.) Anyway, Anna and I both took our creed from Forster: "Personal relations are the real life." Now, GT was telling me Christianity exalted the same thing. It only made sense that personality would be attributed to God.

GT: You see why all this is such a problem for our friend No Name?

GPL: Not with you...

GT: Well, to have a name is to be particular: an individual person. I, Gilbert, can be in personal relationship with you, Geoffrey. I can laugh with you, cry with you...

GPL: Fight with me.

GT: Yes. It's the fighting No Name wants to avoid. One can understand why. All those ICBMs you mentioned. Verdun. The Inquisition...

He shuddered again.

GT: The universe can't fight with the universe. He's perfectly right there. If we all merge into the universal goo, there'll be no more war.

GPL: And no more personal relations.

GT: Right. No affection. No struggle. No growth. No thinking—hence no disagreeing. But most importantly: no freedom and no love...

It takes two to love. It takes two to fight. There's no getting around it. To have one is always to invite the possibility of the other. Without some kind of separation, division—all those potentially tragic things—love is totally impossible.

That's why No Name found me arrogant—for suggesting Christianity is not the same as every other religion. That it's actually different from his Eastern monist philosophy. And is indeed greater. *Non mea culpa.*

The Sphinx paused for a moment, looking sadly into the fire. I stared out at the snow. Presently, he said, "For the sake of 'Political Correctness and Universal Harmony,' I'm supposed to agree with him and apologise for my divisive ways. What can I say? *Non mea culpa.*"

Obviously, I didn't buy everything GT said about Christianity. Still, he helped me to see Anna's religion a bit more clearly. If this was what Christianity really was, maybe I should be grateful. At least, I didn't have to endure all that New Age stuff about being doomed by fate—our natal Mercuries being jammed. I was definitely curious now. Perhaps GT was some kind of answer to my prayer. Maybe God was listening to me, after all.

"So you're saying Christianity is different because it honours personality," I said.

"Yes—and human personality, which is central to the Mystery of the Incarnation." With that, GT's voice changed and he recited a verse from the Gospel, with utmost reverence:

Behold, a virgin shall conceive in her womb, and she shall give birth to a son. And they shall call his name Emmanuel, which means: *God with us.*

"But Christianity is more than just that—isn't it?" I said. "It's all this bloody, awful stuff about flailing a man till he's half dead, then nailing him up on a cross. Glorifying torture. I'm sorry, GT, but it's always struck me as grotesque. God punishing his only son—what's that got to do with *love*?!"

GT: Punishing? You may be mixing up Calvin with Catholicism. We'll get back to that one. Anyway, it's all to do with those damnable ICBMs you mentioned. It's like in Kubrick's *2001: A Space Odyssey.* You've seen it, I think?

GPL: Yes, but—?

GT: The monkey becoming man in the first scene at the dawn of time...

GPL: Yes, he takes a bone as the first tool—and then bashes in the skull of another ape. Or proto-human, I suppose.

I recalled the film. After the ape has used that first, primeval tool to kill, he throws it up in the air and the scene cuts to a space station shaped like the bone. It was cleverly done—four million years of human evolution in just two shots. "The beginning of both human technology—and human warfare," I said.

"Indeed," GT replied. "Kubrick's got something like Forster there: another small, secular glimmer of Christianity. Even if it's hardly an accurate reflection of Genesis. Really, I wish I didn't have to rely on all these secular references. But what's a man to do in a culture like this? 'When in Rome'..."

GT sighed again. I was lost—and said so.

GT: To clarify: it's a certain limited approximation of the fall into Original Sin at the dawn of time. Humanity has long been savage—all those ICBMs are only a vast, technological amplification of our original fall into violence, long, long ago.

GPL: Excuse me, precisely what has this got to do with Jesus being crucified?

GT: Everything, *absolutely everything*. But you must be patient with an old man, if only for Anna's sake.

GPL: I'm sorry, GT, you're helping me. I want to listen, really. I trust you if you say Christians make a connection between the original—what was that?

GT: Well, in 2001 it's the original act of human violence. But in the Bible, it's Cain and Abel. Christians link that to Original Sin and the parents of the human race.

GPL: Adam and Eve and the Apple. The fruit of the Forbidden Tree.

GT: Yes, the myth of creation in Genesis and the Fall of Creation.

GPL: You call it a myth? Are you saying it's not real?

GT: Only a literalist mind would think that myths aren't real! The Genesis myth points to a far more profound level of reality than mere facts: the origin of the world—and the corruption of the world by the Serpent, with humanity choosing to follow the Serpent.

This is the nature of the Bible. It begins with Creation wounded in Genesis and it ends with the Apocalypse—the Heavenly Jerusalem, Creation healed. All things made new. Where even the lion will lie down with the lamb. In other words, where the instinct to violence has been thoroughly transmuted. Till only love remains.

The Crucifixion is a necessary stage in that Cosmic Redemption.

GPL: But why on earth...?

GT: Ultimately, that's a mystery beyond comprehension.

GPL: That sounds pretty lame. Some might even say it's a cop-out.

GT: Suppose we take it in stages, step by step? Are you willing to bear with me?

GPL: I'll try.

GT: Let's start with the idea that humanity is sick. And being sick, humanity commits evil, countless acts of evil and always has done since the dawn of time.

GPL: Okay, I can handle that.

GT: All those countless acts of evil add up to something, wouldn't you say?

GPL: I'll say... awful misery for the whole human race.

GT: Not only the human race, but animals, the environment. We're poisoning trees, the oceans, everything these days. Soon, it'll be outer space. (Assuming our civilisation doesn't collapse before then.)

GPL: No argument there, either.

GT: Humanity is responsible then, collectively responsible. Simple justice requires that humanity be held *accountable*.

GPL: Okay, I see your logic. Accountability is important.

GT: Indeed. One might even say humanity has a debt to pay. This exploitation of the world and its creatures carries a price-tag. Sooner or later, all of us must confront what we've done. In the East, they call it karma. Every action calls forth its opposite reaction. But the same idea holds true in Christianity. "As ye sow, so shall ye reap," as St. Paul says. There's a certain agreement between the world's religions here: The universe just works like that. Fairness, justice is at the root of God's Creation.

GPL: All right. I don't know if I buy universal karma and all that jazz. But if you have a religious framework like that, what you're saying makes sense: humanity must pay a price for what it's done.

GT: Yes. But here's the rub—*humanity is bankrupt*. There's no way humanity can pay this cosmic, collective debt. Humanity *ought* to be accountable—but what if there's no way humanity *can* be accountable? What if we're just too broken, weak—fallen—to have the least hope of setting things right again?

GPL: You're saying God becomes human so that humanity can be accountable?

GT: Put in purely human terms, yes. Of course, there is no way this unfathomable immensity can be articulated in crude human terms. By becoming human—taking on the sin of the world—God restores the cosmic "balance sheet." That's just another crude metaphor, of course. In the Gospel, it's described as "ransom." In Catholic theology, it's called the "theory of satisfaction." The Creed simply says: *Crucifixus etiam pro nobis sub Pontio Pilato, passus et sepultus est.*[1] But, of course, the Mystery of the Crucifixion is beyond all human words...

As he started speaking the Latin, GT bowed his head solemnly before the crucifix. His voice became filled with reverence as he continued.

GT: Yes. God—as a human being—now carries the Cross of the world that humanity could never carry by itself. In other words, all the horror, all the misery, all the terror humanity has ever inflicted—on itself and every other form of life—is now BORNE by God made man. *That* is the Crucifixion.

GPL: I can't say I'm convinced. Still, it makes more sense than all that jazz about God punishing Jesus—an innocent victim.

GT: If you look into it, I think you'll find that's more a Protestant interpretation than a Catholic one. That's the problem people have growing up in places like England or America. Everything gets mixed-up. People think of something as Christian, when, really, it's just Protestant-Christian. And Protestantism is only thirty percent of worldwide Christianity. They have absolutely no idea the other seventy percent—mainly Catholic and Orthodox—believes something completely different. As a result, Catholicism is deeply misunderstood. The Reformation has a lot to answer for.

---

[1] For our sake he was crucified under Pontius Pilate; he suffered death and was buried.

GPL: Sounds like you have a problem with Protestants then?

GT: Not as individuals! God knows every authentic Christian witness is needed these days. Obviously, there are countless great Protestant witnesses to Christ. But I do get grumpy with the Reformation at times. I confess it. *Mea culpa*. I must be more gentle.

Still, you must realise, Luther initiated the Reformation in protest—antagonism even—towards the Catholic Faith. By doing so, he rejected aspects fundamental to our entire faith. For instance, he rejected the sacred system of Seven Sacraments. Likewise, devotion to the Blessed Virgin Mary and the Communion of Saints, as well as praying for the souls of the faithful departed in Purgatory. People forget these things, my dear man. (But you wouldn't, if you were in Purgatory!)

Forgive me, if I get upset sometimes. The foundation of everything I and countless Catholics believe in, has been compromised. But yes, I must be gentle. Many great Protestants put us Catholics to shame…

Anyway, I beg you to remember: I'm putting all this in the crudest, most simplistic terms. Our minds are too weak to understand what's truly at stake here—a tremendous mystery. That may sound "lame" to you. To my mind, it's just humble to admit that.

But you're right. This has nothing to do with punishing a helpless, innocent victim. It's about mercy, mercy on a cosmic scale. God chooses to assume the entire human condition. That includes death—and it includes being persecuted at the hands of evil. We all die in this world. We are all persecuted by evil. Christ enters into the deepest solidarity with every one of us.

ET VERBUM CARO FACTUM EST, *et habitavit in nobis.*[2]

I nodded, automatically. Still, I had to admit something. This version of Christianity was not only new to me—it didn't strike

---

[2] And the Word was made flesh and dwelt amongst us (from the prologue of St. John's Gospel, enunciated at the close of the Tridentine Latin Mass).

me as goofy. I, too, never liked the New Age goo: all this mindless positive thinking. Here was something serious, at least. It spoke to the existential suffering of the human condition—rather than avoiding it. Whilst Christianity still seemed highly improbable to me, it wasn't quite so ridiculous. I tried to find words to thank the old man. But they didn't come out.

At that point, GT offered to make me some tea, which I happily accepted. I stood up, needing to stretch, and walked over to the ancient gramophone in the corner. An old Harry Belafonte 78 RPM record was lying on the turntable.

"Do you mind if I play this for a moment," I asked GT. "I've always wanted to hear one of these old things."

"Go right ahead."

I wound it up and placed the needle on the vinyl. But what came out was downright peculiar. It sounded like a high-pitched wail and it went like this:

> Pelagius lived in Kardanoel
> And taught a doctrine there
> How whether you went to Heaven or Hell
> It was your own affair.
> It had nothing to do with the Church, my boy,
> But was your own affair.
> Oh, he didn't believe
> In Adam and Eve. He put no faith therein!
> His doubts began
> With the fall of man
> And he laughed at original sin.
> With my row-ti-tow, ti-oodly-ow
> He laughed at original sin.

"That's not Harry Belafonte!" I said, lifting the needle.

"Isn't it? Oh no, that's the Pelagian drinking song by Hilaire Belloc. Different HB. Sorry about that. I do get mixed up sometimes."

I stared down at the faded record label. It said: *The Pelagian Drinking Song* by Harry Belafonte. What on earth was going on here? I put the needle down again, just to make sure I was hearing correctly. Once more, the same screeching wail rang through the room:

And thank the Lord
For the temporal sword
And howling heretics too.
And all good things
Our Christendom brings
But especially barley brew!
With my row-ti-tow
Ti-oodly-ow
Especially barley brew!

GT handed me my tea. "He's making light of very serious things. Heaven. Hell. Original Sin. The idea you can get by without the Church. Perhaps too light. Still, we human beings need a sense of humour. Life on earth would be unbearable without it. No doubt that's why God gave it to us."

What could I say? After that song—if that's what it was—words utterly escaped me.

GT: Belloc needed that outlet, I think. Because if anyone was truly serious, it was Belloc. He was a prophet, profoundly awake to the course the world was taking. He knew what would happen to men, women, and children, if we didn't change that course. And his heart bled because of it. He also saw all this Pelagian stuff coming—the New Age.

GPL: Pelagian? What exactly does it mean?

GT: Oh, it refers to Pelagius. Like in the song. He was an early heretic—one of your countrymen from the fifth century. Perhaps a contemporary of St. Patrick. But he preached a very different creed to St. Patrick's!

According to him, people don't need grace. They don't need the Sacraments. Or the Church. It's all there for nothing, apparently. Forgive me, I'm losing my patience again. Still, it's a serious matter. Very serious. Today, people in Ireland are choosing Pelagius over Patrick. The New Age over the Church. Belloc was already alert to that danger, long ago, when most people were fast asleep. Anyway, I digress. Where were we?

GPL: I don't know. But I was trying to tell you something before, about Anna and me. You're really helping. Obviously, I don't agree with many things you say. But it does help me to understand her better. Thank you.

GT: Well, I'm glad if it helps. Still, I see you're having problems. At best, I'm making Christianity more intelligible for you—but hardly convincing.

GPL: Yes, that's right. I mean, I can almost believe there's a God. And it's not difficult to accept humanity is "fallen," as you put it. It's pretty obvious our species is messed up. Insane, even. If you want to call that "Original Sin," I'm okay with that. But even if I did believe God became human to help us out, why should I believe it was Jesus? Why not Buddha or Krishna or somebody else I never heard of?

GT: Our Lord Jesus Christ said: "Behold I make all things new…" Neither Buddha, nor Krishna, nor any other religion claims its founder said that. Still, that doesn't really answer your question.

GPL: No, it doesn't.

GT: Why this particular man? Why this particular event in Palestine two thousand years ago? How can I be so sure?

GPL: Yes, exactly, how can you be so sure?!

GT: Only faith can make that leap. Admittedly, there's a welter of circumstantial evidence. But, of course, none of it proves anything.

GPL: Still, I'd like to know what you mean by "circumstantial evidence."

GT: Well, much of it's obvious. *Something* happened two thousand years ago. There was a historical person, Jesus of Nazareth. He had followers. And those followers obviously believed—in great numbers—that he rose from the dead after being crucified. Even the most rationalist critic of Christianity admits that.

GPL: Rose from the dead still doesn't mean "making all things new."

GT: Of course not. One must enquire deeply. Yet if one studies the Bible—not just the Gospel, but the whole Bible

—one can see how Christ's redemption of humanity was foreseen by the Jewish prophets. At least, that is the faith of the Church.

GPL: Blind faith, some would say.

GT: Some would—but not the intelligent ones. Tradition entails profound insight, indeed genius. For two thousand years, brilliant theologians, philosophers and saints have grappled with the Mystery of the Bible. Profoundly learned, sophisticated people follow in their footsteps today. Alas, theology is often regarded as naive or dumb in modern culture. The boot is on the other leg. Modern culture is too dumb to understand theology.

Still, one can't dispense with faith. Nevertheless, certain supports for faith are possible. The fact that millions upon millions of people took this up and were willing to die for it. That says something. If you're willing to listen, anyway. Also, the Papacy.

GPL: The Papacy?

GT: Well, St. Peter was the first Pope. Peter is *Petrus* in Latin: rock. Our Lord told Peter he was the rock on which he would build his Church. "And the Gates of Hell will not prevail against it." Two millennia later, the Church with her Papacy is still standing.

By comparison, everything else in the West looks transitory. Mighty empires have come and gone. We've passed through Romanism, barbarianism, feudalism, monarchism, imperialism, democracy…

GPL: Democracy isn't finished, yet.

GT: As you say: "Yet." As you well know, democracy is dying. Rule by democratically-elected governments has largely been transferred to mighty banks and corporations now. "It's the economy, stupid." St. John Paul II called that *economicism*—rule by the economy. Slavery to the market. That, too, will pass…

GPL: But not the Church?

GT: No. Yet that still isn't proof either. Even if the Church outlasts 10,000 years of various different institutions, it won't prove the slightest thing.

All the same, you asked me for "circumstantial evidence." Some folk point out the sheer size of the Church. Catholics account for 1.2 billion people on this planet. The Orthodox Churches number another .4 billion. Protestants, by virtue of their Baptism, also belong to the Church (even if they lack most of the other Sacraments and aren't fully integrated into it).

That's over 2 billion people spread across every continent, in every country—at least where the Faith isn't actively forbidden. There's never been anything remotely like that in human history.

GPL: It's impressive, I admit.

GT: But not proof. Still, it's worth thinking about. Ultimately, *there's one stimulus to faith greater than any other.* Alas, you might say it's the Church's "best kept secret." People outside the Church have no idea what we're talking about. They never experience it. At least, not without breaking Church law.

GPL: Never experience what?

GT: Well, the Sacrament, I mean—Holy Communion. People who have the Sacrament testify to its meaning. They go back and back, hungry. Many go every day. Those who don't have it appear impoverished to us.

My mind reeled. Just when his Christianity was starting to make sense to me, we were back to square one.

GPL: I am sorry, GT. I really don't get this. I mean, how on earth does Jesus get turned into something you eat?!

GT: It is a tremendous mystery.

GPL: I'll say!

GT: Tell you what—you'll find a Bible on that stand next to you. Oblige me, would you—read it yourself. Just one bit: John 6:51–61.

Curious, I decided to indulge the old man. Reaching for the Bible, I flipped through the New Testament till I found John's Gospel:

> I am the living bread which came down from heaven. If any man eat of this bread, he shall live for ever; and the bread that I will give, is my flesh, for the life of the world. The Jews therefore strove among themselves, saying: How can this man give us his flesh to eat? Then Jesus said to them: Amen, amen I say unto you: Except you eat the flesh of the Son of man, and drink his blood, you shall not have life in you. He that eateth my flesh, and drinketh my blood, hath everlasting life: and I will raise him up in the last day. For my flesh is meat indeed: and my blood is drink indeed. He that eateth my flesh, and drinketh my blood, abideth in me, and I in him. As the living Father hath sent me, and I live by the Father; so he that eateth me, the same also shall live by me. This is the bread that came down from heaven. Not as your fathers did eat manna, and are dead. He that eateth this bread, shall live for ever. These things he said, teaching in the synagogue, in Capharnaum. Many therefore of his disciples, hearing it, said: This saying is hard, and who can hear it?

I wasn't sure what to say. I liked Tracey. I didn't want to offend him. Finally, I ventured "I am sorry to have to say it, GT. But this sounds stark, raving, cock-a-doodle-loop-dee-do bonkers to me." GT just shrugged.

GT: It was a hard saying then. It's still hard today…

GPL: I am sorry. It's too much. I don't see how anyone in their right mind could possibly take this seriously.

GT: You're confronted with a strange dilemma then, aren't you? Because for two thousand years, people can't have been in their right minds! And yet Christendom included countless brilliant philosophers, writers, artists, poets, scientists, composers and saints. Their faith—along with that of countless lesser souls—built European culture. Go back to old Europe before the Reformation. Everybody, I mean everybody, takes this seriously. Doesn't matter whether you're in Paris, London, Moscow—or Reykjavik for that matter. Right across Europe you have people *eating His Flesh, drinking His Blood*. Even in our tragic condition today, millions of human souls still regularly partake of the Holy Sacrament of the Altar.

His voice had lowered, taking on profound gravitas, as he said those words... "eating His Flesh, drinking His Blood... Holy Sacrament of the Altar."

GT: Martyrs died for this. They're still dying. But to you, it's merely nuttiness—like Scientology or the New Age. Do you suppose future generations will die for No Name's philosophy? Do you think a new civilisation could be built from faith in that?
This is the entire point of the Church. Her *raison d'être*: "The bread that I will give, is my flesh, for *the life of the world...*" This IS Christianity.

Now, I was slightly taken aback by the solemn reverence with which he spoke these words. But, still, I couldn't help objecting.

GPL: Oh, come on. That can't be true. Jesus was a great moral teacher, I'll grant you that. Surely, that's the central message: Love one another. Do unto others what you would have done unto you. Isn't that the point—the Golden Rule?

GT: Yes—but you're forgetting something.

GPL: And that is?

GT: It is actually difficult—tremendously difficult—to love one another. The best most of us manage is maybe our wife and children. And then only half the time at best. As for loving the rest of humanity—forget it! We need *Him, His* Body, *His* Blood.
That's why Christianity isn't just a rule. Or a moral system. "Jesus was a great moral teacher," you said. Well, that's a *nice*, modern, liberal perspective. Deliberately, insincerely, calculated to *mollify* people. "Oh yes, Jesus was a great moral teacher... we can all agree on that." Unfortunately, when you think about it, it doesn't hold water.

Something about the way he said "nice" grated on my ears. I knew, by now, he didn't like that word.

GPL: Aren't you being a bit dismissive? What about some gentleness here?

GT: I said I was gentle; I didn't say I was a fool! Nor will I consent to foolishness! There's tremendous incongruity here. To wit: Jesus was a great moral teacher who claimed to be God, forgave people their sins and told them to drink his blood. You can't be a great moral teacher and complete nutjob at the same time! You can't have it both ways! Either Jesus was—how did you put it?—"stark, raving, cock-a-doo-dle-loop-dee-do bonkers"… or He was someone to follow, to die for, to base an entire civilisation on…

Forgive me, I must repeat myself. This IS Christianity—not the Golden Rule or *any* rules. You can have the Golden Rule without being Christian. You can obey Christian rules and still not belong to the Church.

Eating His Body, drinking His Blood, as Vatican II said, is "the source and summit of the Christian life." The source, the summit. The beginning, the means and the end.

Forgive me, my gentle friend, but I really must be emphatic about this one sole thing. As Benedict XVI said, *the Church simply does not exist without the Eucharist.* It may not be "politically correct"—but it's crucial. Many English people just don't get this. But you will never comprehend your future wife, if you can't understand this.

My future wife?! Who was this fruitcake? But all I did was grunt and say, "I suppose you'd better tell me then."

GT: It's very, very sad. But the English often have the whole idea of the Church mixed-up. You think it's a place where someone preaches a sermon, you sing some hymns, maybe say a prayer or two. Then come home again. For Catholics, that's a travesty of the Church! I warned you this wouldn't be PC—but it's the tragedy of the English-speaking world. Millions and millions of English people—also Americans, Australians, etc.—they all think a church is somewhere you gather on Sundays for spiritual instruction. Rules!

**GPL**: Only English-speaking people think that...?

**GT**: Well, it's not their fault. You have to remember history. The Reformation never took hold in most countries like it did in England. So this state of confusion doesn't exist in Greece or Russia or Spain. Plus, in some countries, they use separate words for Protestant and Catholic sites of worship. But in English, it's just one word—*church*—for two entirely different realities.

To your ordinary American, a church is something like a meeting hall—an assembly room! To a Catholic, it's a place where the most sublime ritual on Earth is enacted. God comes down to earth, bread and wine are transformed that HE might transform us.

He bowed his head with this and his words took on that same solemn tone, as before. Suddenly, a nearby church bell tolled. It was twelve o'clock.

**GT**: You must excuse me for a moment—the Angelus...

**GPL**: The what?

**GT**: I'm not surprised you don't know. Another casualty of the Reformation. Just a moment for prayer, please.

GT rose from his chair, turned to face a small statue of the Blessed Virgin Mary and began praying:

*The Angel of the Lord declared to Mary: And she conceived of the Holy Spirit.*

*Hail Mary, full of grace, the Lord is with thee; blessed art thou amongst women and blessed is the fruit of thy womb, Jesus. Holy Mary, Mother of God, pray for us sinners, now and at the hour of our death. Amen.*

*Behold the handmaid of the Lord: Be it done unto me according to Thy word.*

He then repeated the *Hail Mary*, before bending down on one knee to say:

*And the Word was made Flesh: And dwelt amongst us.*

A third *Hail Mary* followed, before:

*Pray for us, O Holy Mother of God, that we may be made worthy of the promises of Christ.*

*Pour forth, we beseech Thee, O Lord, Thy grace into our hearts; that we, to whom the incarnation of Christ, Thy Son, was made known by the message of an angel, may by His Passion and Cross be brought to the glory of His Resurrection, through the same Christ Our Lord.*

With that, GT sat down with a sigh. "They used to say that all across Ireland," he said to me. "No doubt it protected this island far more than people recognise today."

# VII

## Famished for Christendom

ODD is the only way to describe the happenings in GT's parlour. All those weird people coming and going, the strange clock, that ridiculous song on the turntable and still further bizarre things I haven't told you yet. But what happened then was positively uncanny.

It's hard to explain it exactly. I still felt extraordinarily comfortable sitting by the fire with GT and his cat. And when the old man started praying, I relaxed more than ever. Indeed, the effect of his prayers was soporific. Because, for an instant, I actually fell asleep and began dreaming.

My dream took place inside a large church. And GT was the priest. I realised it was my wedding day and GT was marrying Anna and me. I was standing with him as Anna came towards us down the aisle.

But just as she was about to join me at the altar, she suddenly fled, weeping. I stood there devastated. GT bent over and whispered in my ear, "I'm sorry, GPL. She has to go. She hasn't had enough to eat. She's famished…"

I woke with a start. GT was talking to me. "Your Anna may have a vocation," I heard him saying, "which would of course be the ultimate impediment to you marrying the girl, a divine impediment. But listening to your story, I'm not so sure that's the case here. I wonder if it's more a matter of hunger."

"Hunger?"

"She's hungry in her soul. Honestly, I think she's famished. Famished for Christendom."

"What's that supposed to mean?" I said, flabbergasted.

GT: I'd like to explain it to you, GPL. But it won't be easy for you. It's so utterly alien to your outlook. But if you'll permit me to be frank—even brutally frank—I'll try. I am afraid, though, it may prove difficult to be completely gentle with the truth.

GPL: Go on, hit me with it.

GT: Very well. Anna may not admit it—even to herself—but she longs to marry you. I am sure of it. It isn't you she can't bear. It's your world.

GPL: My world?

GT: Your secular world with its new religion. Your world that claims to stand for equality and rights, but crushes anyone who dares to stand for Christian principles.

This is how she sees it, I'm afraid. Her world has meaning, grace, beauty—*life*. It feeds her soul. Your world leaves her empty, hungry, cold...

Her world—the world of Christendom—built Chartres Cathedral, the Sistine chapel and the Sacré Coeur de Montmartre. Your world builds tower blocks and suburbs and billboards and monotonous offices with cramped little cubicles. Not to mention pornographic television networks.

Your world is dedicated to power, profit, a purely materialist metaphysic.

Her world is dedicated to HIM...

GT bowed his head, once more.

GT: That's why she left in the first place. Ladakh, Hawaii, Ojai, that cabbage patch in Scotland... Back then, she didn't know what she was looking for. Still, she knew she'd never find it in your world.

I wanted to protest. It all seemed so simplistic: demonising modernity, celebrating medievalism. But I kept my mouth shut. Somehow, even though GT had never met Anna, I wondered if he already understood her better than I did.

GT: I warned you I must be frank. Shall I continue?

GPL: Yes, go on.

GT: The good news is this: Anna loves you. The bad news is: she's hungry. She's frightened. Scared that if you and she got together, you'd drag her back to a modern, soulless world she finds hideous. Everything you represent is a threat to her world—for reasons that you must admit are well-grounded in… history.

GPL: History?

GT: Well, we spoke about the 1960s already. But there's 1789 and all that.

GPL: The French Revolution?

GT: Yes, but other revolutions too, including the American. They all shared the same dream. A dream to build a brave new secular world with liberty and justice for all. No more medieval monarchs and Popes running the show. Instead, you got reality TV and a capitalistic super-elite with power, wealth and control beyond any ruler in the Middle Ages…

The snow was falling more gently now. The frankincense burned continuously: oddly, it never seemed to need replenishing. Somebody was playing John Lennon's *Working Class Hero* down in the street. I heard the bit about being doped by sex and TV. And then the line: "You think you're so clever and classless and free" drifted up. It was almost as if GT orchestrated that moment to underscore his point. And then, I actually started wondering if he had. What on earth was I thinking?!

GT: The thing with John Lennon is, he never understood how England got the way it did. It began back in the early 1500s when Henry VIII wanted to get rid of his marriage and made himself head of the English Church, in place of the Pope. Henry made England Protestant—forcibly—destroying the monasteries and killing anyone who opposed him. Once he eliminated all those nuns and monks and prayers and Sacraments, England didn't have the wherewithal to resist the emerging bourgeoisie—the new capitalists. But I ought to stick with your Anna. Anna can't bear this de-sacramentalised world. That's why she's looking for a convent now. But not any old convent you know…

GPL: Yes, I know, one with the Mass in Latin...

GT: Precisely. I don't suppose you know much about Vatican II—or at least what happened after Vatican II?

GPL: Anna has told me a little. That's when they got rid of the old Mass, isn't it? They made a lot of other changes...

GT: Yes, too often, they tried to make the Church into a piece of this world. But your Anna's very sensitive. She can't bear it. Either this modern world or this modern Church. That's why she went to Marseilles.

GPL: You think she's running away from reality then?

GT: I wouldn't call it reality. But yes, she is running. And if you're going to marry the girl, you'll have to provide something better than this wasteland. Otherwise, her soul will waste away...

GPL: Marry her! What can I give her? I'm not a traditional Mass-going Catholic!

GT: Well, you could start with sympathetic understanding for her predicament. You told me you can't fathom her whole way of life now. Her religion, her thinking, her politics. But it was always like this, wasn't it? Anna has *never felt at home in this world*, your world, the one you champion.

GPL: I don't champion this world. There are plenty of things wrong with it!

GT: Well, to Anna's thinking, at least, you champion the things that made this world what it is. To her mind, you defend the Secular Religion that built this world—plus the glue that keeps it together. Of course, if you don't even see you have a religion, it's not easy to appreciate that. But I'm sorry, it gets worse...

GPL: Worse? Oh, great.

GT: Your world, your religion *destroyed her world*—Christendom. That's why Anna likes Ireland, you see—it hasn't quite succeeded here, yet. Almost, but not quite. The Faith is on its knees in Ireland. But it's not dead, not yet. Anna would do anything to save this country...

I was astounded. Had he met Anna somewhere, but hadn't told me? Because what he said about her sounded right. She did hark back to the old medieval world of Christendom—when all of Europe belonged to one faith. All sorts of things started falling into place now. Half-remembered things Anna told me. Old pieces of history I'd forgotten. A Cambridge lecture I once attended about Max Weber and his book *The Protestant Work Ethic and the Spirit of Capitalism*. I recalled, too, what GT said earlier about the Enlightenment or "Age of Reason" leading to the French Revolution.

A timeline began taking shape in my mind. Anna's timeline, her version of history at least. And it looked like GT's too. According to their version, things started going wrong in 1517 with Luther and the Reformation. Then, Henry VIII took over the English church, forcefully converting people to the new religion. Europe separated into two spheres—a northern Protestant one and a southern Catholic one.

I was beginning to see that, for GT, this fact had led to very crucial distinctions, not just in religion, but in every aspect of culture. Two very different psychologies emerged between nations that remained faithful to the older Catholic tradition and those that didn't—indeed which actively protested against that tradition. And the new Protestant sphere went on protesting, went on innovating, went on dismantling tradition. This had led to secularism much more rapidly in the northern Protestant world than the Catholic one.

The northern sphere, particularly England, had also pioneered capitalism. That's what GT meant by capitalist bourgeoisie replacing medieval rulers. Obviously for him, it was all connected to the secularising revolutions. "1789 and all that." The Cultural Revolution of "1968" only built on every revolution that preceded it.

Of course, 1789 had happened in Catholic France, not Protestant Europe! That would seem to throw GT's theories. But, as we continued to speak, I realised that—for GT at any rate—this exception only proved the rule. Violent revolution didn't tend to happen in Protestant countries, precisely because those countries had already undergone the original Protestant revolution—jettisoning tradition. Those countries secularised rapidly, indeed almost effortlessly, compared to Catholic countries.

No, secularism didn't take hold in Catholic countries without revolutionary violence. And France, like other Catholic countries, experienced not only revolution, but also *reaction to revolution*. In France, Catholics resisted the Revolution to protect Christian tradition. They even went to war against the Revolution! Later in our conversation, GT called this resistance "Counter-Revolution." But Counter-Revolution never really featured in the Protestant countries. Generally speaking, they didn't suffer revolutions the same way Catholic countries did. In GT's view, they all too easily accommodated themselves to secularism.

I'm getting ahead of myself, telling you things I only realised later. I only mention them now, because they may help you make sense of GT's thinking—and where our conversation was headed.

To me, everything seemed polarised in GT's head. All black and white. Manichean. Dualistic. Cringeworthy. A "shining city on a hill" versus my ugly, tawdry world of modernity. I can't say I liked it at all. Still, it helped me to understand Anna. I decided to tell him so. "All this makes sense of Anna's politics," I said. "She used to love England. Now, it's like she can't bear her own country…"

GT: Well, in so many ways, England kicked off the process. Henry VIII began the brutal, terrifying assault on Anna's world. The French didn't get in on the act until 1789. Later, there were the Communist Revolutions in Russia, 1905 and 1917.

GPL: Are you saying there's no difference between the French Revolution and the Communist Revolution?!

GT: Of course I'm not saying anything as simplistic as that. There is, however, more commonality than many might suppose. Both were calculated attempts to wipe out the old order. Both were based on egalitarian ideals, but led to genocide. Both tried to kill the Church, destroying churches or expropriating them for secular purposes. Did you know that in both France and Russia they changed the week from seven to ten days?

GPL: What's that got to do with anything?

GT: Well, it eliminates the Sabbath, for a start. All these things—the Reformation, the French Revolution, the Communist Revolution—are united in this: a revolutionary endeavour to destroy the tradition of the Church. Today, things like the ongoing secular and sexual revolutions attempt the same thing. Less violently, it may seem, but the song remains the same.

I am putting it in broad strokes, I admit. We can't do an entire history course here. Still, I hope you can see the links I'm making. Henry VIII's initial destruction of the Church can't be exonerated from the later rise of secularism, capitalism, and many other aspects of modern England.

What was I to say? GT had clearly latched onto my critique of capitalism—and turned it on its head. According to him, capitalism, which I objected to, belonged part and parcel to the secular historical trajectory I supported. I might not like it, but he was making connections that made sense. I couldn't just write them off. Northern Protestant Europe *had* become secular far more quickly than Catholic Europe. And that same Protestant Europe was also the birthplace of capitalism, above all England and the Netherlands. I wanted to challenge him, but the only thing I managed was pretty lame.

GPL: You seem to be mixing up a lot of things here: Protestantism, Secularism, Capitalism. They aren't all the same thing! I am not a capitalist! And even if I agreed there were some sort of secular religion I adhered to, I am not a Protestant. I am not a Christian.

GT: No, but your parents were. Or at least your grandparents. Today's Secular Religion owes much of its DNA to the Reformation. Certainly, it owes a great deal to the original Protestant revolt against the Church. And—France aside—the most secular countries in this world are the formerly Protestant nations.

Look at it this way, if you like. We are speaking of *two worlds* here, two opposed worlds. One world—in Spain, Russia, Ireland, etc.—still possesses the original faith of the Church. It has priests and bishops.

GPL: Sounds like you're polarizing to me. A capitalist world versus the Catholic one.

GT: Not quite. I just mentioned Russia. I might have said Greece as well, which is perhaps the least secularised country in the Western world.

For the sake of simplicity—broad strokes again—think of it as *Sacramental societies versus non-Sacramental ones.* Catholic and Orthodox societies both have the Sacraments. Historically, they're the ones that most potently resisted secularism and capitalism. But other societies like England— deprived of the Sacraments—are the main pioneers of the modern world.

GPL: The Church of England has these Sacraments, doesn't it? They have communion services, stuff like that, don't they?

GT: A special case, there. And a source of much debate. It would take us too far from our point, I think. Let us simply say that the Church of England isn't practicing the *complete* Sacramental system: *all seven Sacraments.* They don't have Confession, for example, which is indispensable for the Sacramental life. It is inconceivable that anyone can practice the Sacraments without absolution! However, it gets far more complicated than that. Suffice it to say that the Magisterium of the Church has determined, for weighty reasons, that most of the Anglican "Sacraments" are invalid.[1]

At that moment, I recognised this was basically the same thing Anna believed. But there was something else. A strange thing Anna said at the farmhouse came back to me. In the past, she had known this New Age teacher—a woman who called herself an "esotericist" and said she saw the angelic kingdoms. The female "esotericist," Anna said, was completely opposed to Catholicism.

---

[1] As GT implies, his statement is simplified for a layman. Some might object that it lacks theological precision. For certain "High Church" Anglicans claim to possess the Sacrament of Confession (having allegedly re-introduced it in restricted circles during the Anglo-Catholic revival of the nineteenth century). However, Anglicans themselves dispute whether their rare practice of confession is a Sacrament or not! Moreover, "Anglican confession" is not an obligation in Anglicanism. Even ignoring the fact that the Church's Magisterium

But this New Age woman appeared to contradict herself. Because she said something very strange regarding angels and the Church. According to her, a special angel was attached to each Catholic priest at the moment of his ordination. And that angel, she said, stayed with him for life, ensuring that the Sacrament always occurred in the Catholic Church—no matter how bad or immoral the priest was. But it wasn't like that in other churches. Anna didn't know what to think. Clearly, she no longer believed in esoteric teachings. Still, Anna said, it wasn't impossible, what this New Age woman said. Perhaps she had seen a glimmer of reality there—that ordination and the other Sacraments were different in the Catholic Church. Under the protection of the angels...

I had drifted off from what GT was saying. "But perhaps I'm getting too technical for you," the old man said, probably noting my mind was elsewhere. "If I may return to my point about you and Anna?"

"Please do," I said with relief.

declared Anglican "Sacraments" (save Baptism and Marriage) to be invalid and taking certain Anglo-Catholic opinions into account, the complete sevenfold Sacramental Mystery has clearly been absent from the lives of the vast majority of Anglicans since the Reformation. Having once been an Anglican himself and having studied in an Anglican college, the author of this book has come to believe—not without genuine pain and regret—that this fact explains much about the Church of England and indeed English society in general. At any rate, GT's broad point about *Sacramental societies (Catholic and Orthodox) versus non-Sacramental societies* should be plain to see.

# VIII

## Talking About
## a Counter-Revolution

MY mind was awhirl. One half of me felt strangely comforted by GT. But the other half was distinctly unsettled by his simplistic, medieval worldview.

Even the room reflected GT's antiquated views. There were that strange clock and gramophone. Likewise, there were framed portraits of people from the past I didn't recognise, although I thought one might be St. Patrick. I hesitated to ask who the others were. One frame was different, though. Instead of a person, it displayed the Irish tricolour flag—with a strange twist. For the central White band of the flag, between the Green and Orange, was not simply blank white. Instead, it featured a red heart with a cross atop. Like everything else in that room, it looked odd to me.

> GT: You and Anna stand for two different worlds, divided for centuries. You, your parents, and their parents stand for the world without the Sacraments. Anna and myself stand for another world—largely conquered today. Conquered, that is, by your de-Sacramentalised world.
>
> We are Catholic traditionalists, which means we hold to tradition, no matter what revolution—Protestant, secular, Communist, etc.—tries to overthrow it. Once there were many millions of us across Europe. Now, we are like the last, scattered remnants of a once-great tribe.
>
> GPL: Many millions? You're kidding me, right?
>
> GT: Well, not in England, of course. Have you ever heard of the Counter-Revolution in France, in Spain, in Catholic countries everywhere?

GPL: I can't say I have.

GT: Well, it started in France after the 1789 revolution. The people rose up to protect Catholic tradition. But they were massacred in scores of thousands. There's a long history of Counter-Revolution we can't go into here. But, in brief, the term refers to *the resistance Catholic cultures always manifested against the mighty secularising revolutions*—both here in Europe and in Latin America.

I shifted in my chair, unsure where he was going with this. I was worried he was right: Anna had joined some bedraggled tribe of hidebound, reactionary types like himself—a dinosaur, like Al said—who could never accept cultural progress. My stomach rumbled. Slightly hungry, I also felt irritated with him. I looked at his venerable timekeeper ticking away in the corner. It was half-past Pius XII o' clock.

"History is written by the victors," GT sighed. "The losers are often expunged and forgotten. You won't hear much about Counter-Revolution, these days. Certainly not in English history texts, at any rate."

At that moment, came a loud rap at the door. GT cried out, "Ah, come in, Colonel, punctual as ever!"

But when the Colonel entered, I hardly knew what to think. His outfit did indeed look vaguely military—polished boots, and a crisp, khaki starched shirt and trousers. On his head, he wore a red beret. A rosary hung around his neck and his breast pocket was marked with an insignia. The insignia was the same red heart with the cross depicted on the centre of GT's Irish flag.

"Here you are, General, your orders. I'm afraid you'll find them a trifle hot to handle," he said, handing him a large plastic bag.

"Thank you, Colonel Wilhelmsen!"

"Anytime, General. ¡Viva Christo Rey!" he exclaimed and saluted GT.

"¡Viva Christo Rey!" GT responded, returning the salute. And with that, the bizarre figure exited as quickly as he had come.

GPL: Who—or, maybe I should say, *what*—was that?

GT: Oh, Colonel Wilhelmsen, you mean?

**GPL:** If that's his name, yes. But what army does he belong to? Wasn't that a uniform?

**GT:** Ah yes, it's the traditional attire of the Carlists.

**GPL:** Carlists?

**GT:** A Counter-Revolutionary army in Nineteenth Century Spain. Like I said, you don't hear much about these things today. But once they fought against godless secularism in Spain. *Viva Christo Rey* was their cry: Long live Christ the King! You hear things like that in Catholic countries. Or you used to. I don't suppose you hear it too often working in London.

**GPL:** Well, no, not really.

**GT:** Or on Wall Street either. London, New York: they may be the capitals of two great empires—but they're not the whole universe, you know!

This was just too much for me. "Please tell me exactly what is a Spanish Counter-Revolutionary Colonel doing here in Ireland? And why does he call you General?"

"Well, for a start, he's not a Spaniard. He's an American, who came over to the cause. Not too many Spaniards are called Wilhelmsen. As for the General part, well, we're all fighting the same battle. Belloc, Chesterton, Wilhelmsen, me…"

I really had no idea what to say to his "explanation." Dumbly, I just asked: "What's in the bag?"

"Ah yes, the hot order. It's getting cold. We'd better eat it. It's lunch—fish and chips! I heard your stomach rumbling—and it's Friday, so I can't eat meat."

"Who else in this Irish town has fish and chips served to them by Counter-Revolutionary soldiers against godless secularism?"

"Why, only me, of course," he said cheerily. "Rank hath its privileges, you know. Anyway, dig in. I think you'll find it's delicious! But first I must say grace."

GT crossed himself and prayed. I looked around the room, half-wondering if there were some hidden camera tucked away and I would end up on some Irish television gag-show. Anyway, I was hungry. I stopped asking questions and ate. On one point, at least, GT and I were agreed. The food was fantastic. The fish, particularly, was sublime—truly out of this world. Honestly, it tasted better than any fish I had ever had.

We ate in silence. Occasionally, GT offered some fish to the cat, who seemed to enjoy it as much as I did. Having finished the meal, I felt deeply satisfied, even peculiarly refreshed. No longer irritated, I wanted to know more about GT's strange world.

But the old man had disappeared into another room to make us tea. I took the moment to glance at his books. Most were by authors unknown to me, although I recognised the works of Tolkien and some by Graham Greene like *The Power and the Glory*. There were also volumes by Belloc and Chesterton he had mentioned. A book called *The Pope's Legion* by someone called Coulombe caught my eye. It detailed the attempt by a multinational army to defend the Papal States from Italian conquest. When GT returned with the tea, I was looking at Tolkien's *The Return of the King*.

"Ah, you've discovered my little Counter-Revolutionary library!" he said. "You've read Tolkien? He was a Catholic monarchist, you know. That book expresses his monarchist yearnings. Poor man felt terribly afflicted by modernity." Then, he added, "All this is quite appropriate for our little discussion concerning Anna, isn't it?"

I couldn't resist being ironic. "Why is it that absolutely *everything* that goes on in this room seems 'quite appropriate' to our little discussion?" I asked.

GT simply shrugged and said, "Just trying to help you out with Anna, my good man."

> GPL: So you're saying Anna's into all your Catholic Counter-Revolutionary stuff against the modern world?
>
> GT: I'm saying Anna now stands for her Irish grandmother's world—the world with the Sacraments.
>
> GPL: How… how did you know Anna had an Irish grandmother? I never told you that!
>
> GT: Didn't you? Perhaps it was some other time. Forgive me, I'm straying from my topic again. My point is—Anna's

apparently irrational reaction to British culture might have more to do with her grandmother than you realise.

GPL: What on earth are you talking about?

GT: Ask Anna. I think you'll find her grandmother's father was murdered by the Black and Tans in County Cork. And that his family nursed a long hatred of British colonisation of Ireland.

He was invoking a long Irish history of which I knew little. I had heard of the Black and Tans. They were the crack forces dispatched by Britain to suppress the Irish, after the Easter Rising in 1916, which led to Irish independence. Anna had never said her great-grandfather was killed by them. I had no idea where he was getting all this stuff. And I didn't think he'd tell me if I asked. I decided to ask Anna first, find out if he was right. Then I could confront him another time. Right now, I felt too bewildered to know what to say. Instead, I tried challenging him on a different tack.

GPL: Something bothers me, GT. You're painting this whole bloody history, going all the way back to Henry VIII. How the British suppressed Catholic Ireland. Isn't this dangerous—particularly for someone who calls himself a "gentle traditionalist"? Inciting all these ancient hatreds...?

GT: I said I was gentle; I didn't say I whitewashed history! Still, my friend, your point is well-taken. There are centuries here, centuries of evil and killing on both sides. Bringing it all up *can* be dangerous. On the other hand, those who forget the past are doomed to repeat it. It's a cliché, I know, but not without truth.

We are engaged in trying to understand things here—including your Anna. Up to now, her mysterious Catholic conversion never made a grain of sense to you, has it? Nor her "bizarre" attitudes to England. I'm just submitting things for your consideration: things that may help you comprehend...

GPL: Okay, go on.

99

GT: As I said, there's a long history here. But it can't be understood without seeing history has two sides: the winners and the losers.

In this case, the loser is the forgotten Sacramental world of the Church. However, it wasn't always forgotten. Once, it was so precious people even took up arms to defend that Sacramental culture. That's what happened in places like Italy, Spain, France. There were actually Counter-Revolutionary armies. As I said before, once there were many millions of us. Millions praying and working for an alternative course into the future, an alternative civilisation to your secular-capitalist civilisation. Praying, working, sometimes even dying.

GPL: Sometimes even killing, by the sound of it.

GT: That is true. Bl. Pius IX did summon an army to defend the Papal States. St. Joan of Arc likewise led armies into battle. There have been occasions when war—as tragic as it is—nevertheless appears to be the will of heaven. Of course, there have been many other times when bloodthirsty "Christians" committed atrocities. That's another discussion. For now, my main point is this: once upon a time, millions upon millions rejected the materialistic civilisation we have today and desperately sought an alternative. That is what Counter-Revolution really means. And whatever impression my Carlist friend may have given you, it has nearly always been about prayer and sacraments, sacrifice and effort. Not militias.

GPL: Okay. I see we can't get into obscure military history. You're trying to help me understand Anna and her attitudes about Ireland.

GT: That's right, but even in Ireland, we can't completely avoid these things. These days, the Irish Rising of 1916 against Britain is usually considered along ethnic or nationalist lines. What is too easily forgotten is that nearly all the rebels were Catholics permeated with a mystic Catholic vision of nationhood. Ireland, they believed, had a spiritual mission. By contrast, they regarded England as the site of a decadent capitalist culture, which denied Ireland her true calling. Patrick Pearse, the spiritual leader of the 1916 Rising, believed that British culture, British education was murdering the Irish soul. He thought God intended something very different for Ireland than the materialism of the British Empire.

GT sighed. "Pearse, Plunkett, MacDonagh, among others—I doubt the names mean anything to you—were men who cared enough about these things to voluntarily sacrifice themselves in an utterly futile battle with the British Empire. They were rounded up in a week and shot by the British—as they fully realised they would be. Still, their courage changed everything." For a long time, he stared into the fire, before murmuring, in a low voice, words from long ago:

> I write it out in a verse:
> MacDonagh and MacBride
> And Connolly and Pearse
> Now and in time to be,
> Wherever green is worn,
> Are changed, changed utterly:
> A terrible beauty is born.

"What's that?" I asked.

"It's 'Easter 1916,' a poem by William Butler Yeats, commemorating the rebels who immolated themselves to save the soul of Ireland," he said wistfully.

Then a bounce returned to his voice: "Yet one must remember what happened after Ireland achieved independence in 1922! When the Irish formed their own state, they *thoroughly rejected* the more secular orientation of the British. Instead, Ireland became a country which *culturally protected Catholic Christian principles*— rather than protecting the values of the emerging Secular Religion! In this sense, one might even say Ireland was once more counter-revolutionary than revolutionary. But when I asked you earlier about Counter-Revolution you had hardly heard the word. Isn't that right?"

"True," I admitted.

GT: This is the problem living in a world dominated by the Anglosphere. Everything, everything is skewed towards the

Anglo-American establishment. Cultures like Catholic Ireland, Spain, Italy, Poland, France, Latin America tend to get rubbed out. All your media, all your culture, all your history is completely blanketed by "Anglo-Saxon" attitudes.

GPL: That sounds rather extreme, maybe even paranoid.

GT: Is it? If I asked you to name me a hundred British or American pop stars, I'm sure you'd have no problem. How many French or Italian ones do you know?

Same with films and television. Oh sure, a few people—very few—watch some French art films. Most people, though, stick with Hollywood. Or they watch sitcoms and soap operas. How many of those aren't in the English language?

Let me ask you something. This is your first time in Ireland. I don't think you've properly visited a Catholic country before, have you?

I was taken aback. He was right. I'd made a couple of day-trips to France, but that was it. Moreover, I'd visited Protestant, English-speaking parts of Africa. I realised I hadn't experienced anything outside the Anglosphere. And GT seemed to know it…"The world looks different, once you step beyond the world shaped by Britain and her former colonies," GT said. "That's partly what happened to your Anna. She travelled. It started breaking down her cultural prejudices."

What GT said was sobering. Maybe my attitudes were too narrowly English. I'm ashamed to say that before GT raised the issue, I'd never considered it before.

"Also," GT continued, "that convent in Marseilles helped Anna to understand the French Counter-Revolution. By the time she got to Ireland, she understood the Catholic culture here much better as a result."

"Is that what that flag is about?" I asked, pointing to his strange Irish tricolour. "That Carlist officer had the same thing on his shirt…"

"Yes, it's the Sacred Heart of Jesus. The original tricolour was French: a symbol of the Revolution. But the Catholic French who resisted the Revolution wore the Heart of Jesus on their lapels. Later, they placed it on the flag. It seems they meant to 'baptise' the revolutionary tricolour, Christianise it. There were similar initiatives elsewhere, not just in Ireland, but also Belgium, Quebec and other places. Oddly enough, though, it seems the Irish may have had the idea first, even before the French. Back in 1641, an Irish Catholic Confederation tried rising up against the British—and the Confederation placed the Sacred Heart on their seal. It's a clear antecedent to placing the heart on the flag."

GT's eyes twinkled. "No one ever tried putting the Sacred Heart on the Stars and Stripes or the Union Jack, of course."

Seal of Irish Catholic Confederation, circa 1640s
with very early representation of the Sacred Heart
at the bottom surmounted by flames and cross.

His point was taken. In England, the idea would be completely unthinkable—like something from beyond Pluto. But, obviously, certain Catholic countries were once very different from England. Earlier, I had judged GT's decor as odd. Perhaps it was. Or perhaps GT was right: my cultural prejudices prevented me from recognizing the legitimate aspirations of a society different from my own.

In any case, GT was helping me to comprehend the change that had happened to Anna during her journeys abroad. I admitted that to him.

"Yes, she's alienated from your world," GT replied. "Anna has become a modern-day Counter-Revolutionary."

"Yikes! You're not going to tell me she has to wear that crazy uniform, are you?"

GT roared with laughter. "Not to worry, my good man. Alas, perhaps I've emphasised the military side of things too much. I only wanted to show that—once upon a time—people in Catholic countries *cared* about very different things than they do now. But armies are necessarily tragic things. No, no, the vast majority of Counter-Revolutionaries never wore a uniform. Again, they prayed and worked—*ora et labora*—for a different culture than we have today. At any rate, the main threat to Catholic values today is not military conquest. It comes from elsewhere."

Abruptly, we were interrupted. Heavy thuds came from the stairwell. The door was thrown open, as a short, dark-skinned man with a heavy black moustache burst into the room. Frantically waving his arms around, he fell to his knees at GT's feet, wrapped his short arms around his legs and wept uncontrollably. I could just about make out some words, barely intelligible in Spanish, I think, between his sobs.

"Por los corazones de Jesús y María," the weeping figure implored, "Señor Valentino, haz algo. Por los niños, por los niños…"

GT: English, please, Brother Juan-María. We are not alone. I am busy with this gentleman here.

J-M: Oh, I am sorry. I was so distressed, I did not see you. I can come back later, if you like.

GT: We can spare a moment, can't we, GPL?

GPL: Yes, of course.

GT: Tell me what is wrong, Juan-Maria. Briefly. I will mull it over and see you tomorrow.

J-M: It's the children in the school! The children! But not just in the school—everywhere you go now. They are becoming possessed by unclean spirits! ¡Caramba! They have all these iPods and X-Boxes and smartphones and mutant ninja turtles. They never play with each other anymore. They just absorb all this American rubbish! Soon, they'll be just like American children. Do you know Americans have to give their children drugs to pacify them? Ritalin and other things? It's terrible! It's terrible! You must come and help the children, Señor Valentino!

GT: We must all do what we can, Juan-Maria. I am in Ireland right now. I mustn't forget the Irish children, either.

J-M: Yes, yes. The Irish children. They have it even worse! They speak the same language! They have no protection at all... ¡Caramba! Si, si, Señor. You must help the Irish children. Use your ring to exorcise their schools! But then, I beg you, please come to Spain.

GT: I will be there tomorrow!

J-M: Thank you! Thank you, Señor Valentino!

With that, Juan-Maria took GT's outstretched hand with the ring and started kissing it.

J-M: If I only had a ring like yours, I could chase the unclean spirits away.

GT: Now, Juan-Maria, you know you cannot use my ring. But you have prayer. You have Holy Water. It is very effective, you know.

J-M: I am sorry, Señor. I get so worried about my children in the school... children everywhere!

GT: Worry will not help them. But the situation is grave, I know. Be assured of my assistance.

J-M: All right. I see you are busy now... thank you again, Señor Valentino!

With that, Brother Juan-Maria took my hand and shook it. "Do you have a school, too? He can exorcise it, too, you know!" And then he bent down and whispered in my ear: "They say his ring contains the relics of the True Cross, the Holy Blood and fifteen Roman martyrs."

With that he departed as hurriedly as he had arrived. I looked up at GT. He looked stricken. "It is indeed terrible what is happening to the children," he said. "No-one seems to realise the damage being done. Everyone is asleep! But Brother Juan-Maria is not asleep. His heart is wide-awake."

GT said nothing more. We both stared into the fire for a long time. Finally, I said:

GPL: Why did he call you Señor Valentino? I thought your name was Tracey.

GT: It is. At least, when I'm in this part of the world. Do you ever think about the children, my friend?

GPL: I guess I don't think about them enough.

GT: The children... consumed by the capitalist, materialist order liberated by your Secular Religion. Anyway, where were we?

I couldn't help but bring the conversation back to Anna. It was my favourite subject, of course: Anna... and myself.

GPL: You were saying Anna can't bear my world. That she has these Irish ancestral memories or something, her great-grandfather killed by the Black and Tans... I have to say it kind of makes sense.

GT: Yes, Ireland is at work in Anna's soul. St. Patrick's fire. Blanking-out Irish history won't help things—despite the rage for Political Correctness.

Indeed, Political Correctness is a tool to whitewash what's happening here. Centuries of conflict between two opposed worlds. But it's not simply Ireland. What happened between Britain and Ireland only reflected a greater conflict: the struggle between Christendom and the New World Order. Or, as I put it earlier: *Sacramental society versus non-Sacramental society.*

GPL: Honestly, GT, aren't you putting things a bit too black and white?

GT: Well, again, it's just broad strokes. Our time is limited. I can't present a doctoral thesis here. But if you'll bear with me, you may find it's relevant to Anna.

GPL: Go on, then.

GT: Splendid. So on the one hand, you had the British Empire spanning a quarter of the world's land surface. From Britain to Australia to Canada. In between, you had

Hong Kong, Singapore, India, major chunks of Africa and plenty more. Famously or infamously, the sun never set on the British Empire...

That empire was built on trade, commerce. In its time, it was the greatest capitalist success the world had ever known.

On the other hand, there was Ireland. *She never shared that driving mercantile thrust of the English.* When the Irish went abroad, they didn't try to export capitalism, but Catholicism. The Irish practically built the Church in places like America and Australia.

In short: Ireland once possessed a very different spirit to the rest of the English-speaking world. Unlike that world, she was Catholic. Prayer mattered much more to her than profit.

I can vouch for that. I still remember what Ireland was. Fifty years ago, ninety percent of the Catholic population went to Mass weekly and Confession monthly. A huge section of the population went to both even more frequently. There was a vast populace regularly *cleansed* by the Sacraments.

The children had so much back then. Children had crucifixes in their rooms, even Holy Water. Now, they have Homer Simpson.

Today, the Irish have surrendered *gold*. They've exchanged gold for *plastic*...

GT paused somberly. Tears were falling from his eyes, but he wiped them with a handkerchief from his breast pocket.

GT: Forgive me, I'm losing my thread here. My real point here isn't Ireland and England. It's what they represent. Like I said before: two opposed worlds—Christendom and that other one.

What I'm saying has happened everywhere. We've transited from one type of civilisation, Christian, to another: the secular-capitalist order of modern times. Ireland, of course, is only a microcosm of the bigger picture. Still, in Ireland, the transformation happened within fifty years! People as old as I am still remember what Ireland was—a last, lonely outpost of Christendom. Most other places are different. You can't see the transition from devout Catholic Christendom to secular capitalism in your own lifetime. It took the English 400 years. It took the French 200 years. But in Ireland, the trajectory was compressed into a single lifetime. People went from Jesus Christ to Homer Simpson—just like that. Once there was culture, now there's just this universal...

GPL: "Dumbing down"?

GT: Yes, "dumbing down," as people say now. But let's speak English, shall we? You see those portraits on the wall?

I had, of course, seen them from the start. But it was only now I thought to ask, "Who are they?"

"They represent 1600 years of Irish saints and righteous people—beginning with St. Patrick's arrival in AD 432," GT told me. He then related some names and dates. Apparently, they were arranged chronologically from left to right on the wall: St. Patrick, St. Brigid, St. Columba, St. Dymphna, St. Malachy, Daniel O'Connell, Ven. Matt Talbot..."

Nearly all were portraits. But at the far right was a photograph of a man with a long face and glasses. "Who's the one in the photo?" I asked.

"Ah, that's Dev—Éamon de Valera! Founding father of the Irish nation. Along with Patrick Pearse, he was another key figure of the 1916 Rising in Dublin against the British," GT replied. "He was also very devout. Went to Mass every day. When he was president of the country, the Blessed Sacrament was installed in his home and he visited it five times a day. In 1928, he even had a vision of Christ at Blackrock College, Dublin. Truly, he was completely different from political leaders elsewhere. Like Patrick Pearse before him, Dev likewise believed Ireland had a spiritual mission—which must be protected from Anglo-American materialism. Anyway, the people in those pictures reveal sixteen centuries of tradition. The Irish once revered them. But people prefer other pictures on their wall now. Usually, they're English or American: The Beatles, James Dean, Homer Simpson..."

All this was too much for me. I surrendered to sarcasm. "So it's just the big, bad Anglo-American establishment versus your precious Ireland, is it?"

GT: Well, let's stay with your Anna, shall we? Whether I am right or wrong, she does see it somewhat like that—yes.

Of course, she doesn't remember the Ireland I do. But her grandmother did. If you'll ask her, I think you'll find her grandmother had a profound effect on her during those childhood holidays in County Cork. She even took her to Mass when she was a little girl. Thanks be to God—all this later helped to liberate her from the New Age movement.

I gasped. However GT knew this, it all made sense. It was as if, one by one, the pieces of a puzzle were dropping into place. Before, I was bewildered by how easily Anna had dumped the New Age for Roman Catholicism. All her New Age friends thought she'd completely lost her mind. For them and me, her transition was very difficult to understand. But this Irish Catholic grandmother certainly helped to explain things.

GT: Like I say, Anna's grandmother's father was killed by British troops after 1916. You call me black and white, GPL. It doesn't get much more black and white than that. We are dealing here with ancestral memories wherein Catholic Ireland was brutally colonised by Protestant England.

GPL: Yes, and surely it's very dangerous to revive all that with this polarising, demonising talk!

GT: Dangers lurk everywhere. All this "niceness," this Political Correctness is likewise dangerous. It stops people getting at the truth. Blanderising history doesn't help.

GPL: There's no such word as blanderise!

GT: Well, perhaps there ought to be! In our nice, politically correct, blanderised world, everyone assumes secularism just emerged freely and naturally. Or that the capitalist system that now dominates the West is "just normal." TINA: There Is No Alternative, as your Mrs. Thatcher liked to say.

GPL: She's not my Mrs. Thatcher!

GT: Well, my real point is what Thatcher stood for: the Anglo-American way is the only way. But there *are* alternatives! Whether we like it or not, history has witnessed a raging conflict between competing visions. The Irish who rebelled in 1916 regarded Britain as a decadent, materialistic power. They believed Ireland had a different calling. The Catholic rebels who commandeered the buildings in Dublin prayed the Rosary on the hour, every hour. Did you know that?

**GPL:** I can't say I did.

**GT:** Well, I can't say I blame you. Most Irish don't know that now. Nor do they understand Ireland's spiritual mission. Your Anna understands, however. Her grandmother connects her to a past when children had Christ on the Cross above their beds—not Homer Simpson.

**GPL:** Just what *is* it with you and Homer Simpson?!

**GT:** Well, he's just a form of shorthand: a symbol of modernity. Homer Simpson represents the current state of society quite well, I think. But he's also a symbol for a different kind of colonisation. Not as brutal as the Black and Tans—but more insidious and even more effective.

You see, my friend, I am old. Older perhaps than you think. I remember a time when your media did not exist.

Obviously, he was exaggerating. Still, I could see his point. GT might be a hundred years old, for all I knew—born in the First World War. Certainly, newspapers and magazines existed back in those days. A few jerky silent movies were around. But even commercial radio didn't exist back then. In one lifetime, the old man had seen it all: radio, gramophones, "talkies," colour movies, then television, video, Walkmans, computers and computer games, iPods, the internet, now smartphones and social media, Facebook and Twitter...

**GPL:** I have to admit you've seen a lot of changes.

**GT:** Yes, by the time you were born in 1986, all this technology was pretty much in place. And the propaganda circulating through it was firmly planted in your cultural bloodstream.

My birth year! But before I could open my mouth, he was off and running again.

GT: Once upon a time, Ireland was culturally protected. Back then, that was *what the people wanted*. De Valera stood for that—and they repeatedly elected him leader. Yes, Ireland was so very, very different to our modern, secularised society. Humility, piety, chastity, self-sacrifice were values cherished in Catholic Ireland. Gold, the people had gold. Now, it's the opposite: self-aggrandisement, cynicism, hedonism, and consumer greed. Fool's gold...

In Anna's view, you stand for this decadent world. That world and its power centres—of which the principal ones include Wall Street, London, Hollywood...

That world has overwhelmed Ireland, as it's overwhelming everywhere now. Everything precious to people like Anna is being corrupted, destroyed.

The Church, which should be standing up to it, instead has pop music, pop priests, pop liturgy. That's why your Anna wants to run away to a Latin Mass convent in France—or Ireland, if one can be established here.

She's famished, like I say, famished for a culture your world destroyed. That's the real reason she won't marry you. It's not you. It's this world that's crushed everything she holds dear. And the fact that you stand for it.

His words hit me in the guts. They were devastating. They contained too much truth to easily ignore. His voice took on a softer tone.

GT: I am sorry to be so blunt. It's not as gentle as I would like. Still, I think there's no hope for Anna and yourself unless you really understand this. Whether it's true or not doesn't matter for the moment. This is how she sees the situation.

# IX

## Catholic Horror Stories...
## and More

HEARING all this, I felt frustrated, even angry. All day long, GT had built up this big rosy picture of the Catholic Church. And just how really, really great it all was. Now I had to hear how Anna couldn't marry me, because my world was destroying her precious Church.

It was starting to sound like Anna's grand conspiracy theory. All these interlinked forces working to crush Catholicism. Until now, I had been polite. I had held my tongue. I hadn't told GT I wasn't just some simple-minded dupe of the global elites. Or Freemasons. Or Space Invaders from Planet Zok. Whatever.

Because whoever you blamed, surely the Catholic Church had serious problems of its own. And it had done for centuries. The Crusades. The Inquisition. Now, it was sexually abusing children. Whatever next?! Why was I putting up with all this?

And even if all these truly evil things didn't exist, the Church had other issues, too. Like homophobia. Also latent misogyny, just like Al warned me. Why wouldn't the Church ordain women priests? What on earth was the problem, unless Catholicism was anti-woman? In short, I decided it was high-time I challenged the old man.

> GPL: Okay—that's the way Anna sees it. And you see it. I get that. But how about the way other people see it? Is everybody else just plain wrong? Some people would say Christianity—not just the Catholic Church—has lost all credibility for the crimes it's committed. You sound like there's just this terrible, decadent modern world savaging your poor, innocent Church!

GT: None of us are innocent since the Fall. The Church is both a transcendent mystery and a very human, broken thing. At one and the same time. The human side of the Church is far, far from innocent. At times, it's been positively, diabolically evil.

He shuddered once more. So violently, I couldn't help but reach out to him again.

GPL: What is it? Are you okay?

GT: I couldn't help thinking of the St. Bartholomew's Day Massacre.

GPL: I've heard of that. It was in France, wasn't it?

GT: Yes, on the Feast of the Saint, 23rd August 1572, during the French wars of religion. Thousands of French Protestants massacred. Evil, unspeakable evil...

GPL: So you can understand it when people get angry at Catholics?

GT: I understand the pain, certainly. I promised you we'd talk about these things. Every Catholic needs to confront them. We need to face the suffering of everyone who has been molested, raped, tortured, slaughtered at the hands of Catholics. St. John Paul II saw that clearly and he repeatedly asked for forgiveness—

GPL: Isn't that a bit late now?

GT: Nothing can ever undo the agony those people endured, of course. But it's no good if we Catholics deny the truth. We need to confess that, in countless ways, people have suffered at our hands and still do today.

Here in Ireland, we had sickening abuse of the young. And it was denied. Covered-up by the bishops.

GPL: Exactly. And not just in Ireland.

GT: No, it happened in other countries, too. But in Ireland, it affected maybe as much as four percent of the priesthood. Some of the crimes were monstrous beyond belief. Others somewhat less so. They range from savage rape and violence to touching children through their clothes. Of course, one can never know the psychological damage inflicted by any of these acts. But four percent overall is very high, if true. It was similar in America. In certain other countries too. It may not be as high elsewhere.

**GPL:** It's bad enough wherever it happens.

**GT:** Amen. There is no justification anywhere. There's no defending the indefensible.

**GPL:** Absolutely not!

**GT:** Look, do me one more favour. Earlier, I asked you to read that Bible next to you. Well, there are some newspaper clippings beneath it. If you look, I think you'll find one about Pope Benedict XVI.

I looked under his Bible, curious. "Here it is."

"There's something there he once said on this topic. I marked it. Would you read it, please? I think he expresses what I'm saying much better than I can."

"All right," I said and read it aloud:

> That the power of evil penetrates to such a point in the interior world of the faith is, for us, a source of suffering. On the one hand we must accept that suffering, and on the other, at the same time, we must do everything possible so that such cases aren't repeated. It's also not a motive for comfort to know that, according to sociological research, the percentage of priests guilty of these crimes is no higher than in other comparable professional categories. In any event, one must not stubbornly present this deviance as if it were a nastiness specific to Catholicism.

This surprised me: the former Pope claiming other professional categories were no better than the Catholic Church. It sounded suspicious to me and I told GT so. "I hope you're not going to tell me it's just the media picking on the poor Catholic Church again?"

**GT:** Well, in part, it's just simple mathematics.

**GPL:** Mathematics?

GT: Let's say for the sake of argument that other professional categories do have similar rates. Or institutions besides the Church.

GPL: Okay, for the sake of argument...

GT: Maybe we could even name some of those institutions. Just hypothetically. Have you ever heard of the state of Florisota in America?

GPL: Well, I've heard of Florida, Minnesota... Not Florisota, though. No.

GT: That's good. Because I just made it up. What about the ECB?

GPL: No.

GT: I just made that up, too. It stands for Eternal Christian Brethren. But I remind you, there's no such thing as an ECB.

I felt irritated. Why was he playing these word-games? "I don't mean to play games," he said, as though he'd just read my mind.

GT: What we're talking about is terrible, too terrible for games. At the same time, I'd rather not use real names. Or point the finger at anyone. It's all so appalling. Will you bear with me?

GPL: I'll try.

GT: Good. Now imagine there's a secular juvenile detention system in Florisota that suffered the same terrible thing in the past. Which is not so far from the truth. Because terrible things happen in secular systems, too.

Anyway, we have the FJDS—Florisota juvenile detention system. And the ECB. And they have the same awful thing —professionals who, within those systems, have destroyed children's lives.

GPL: And the point to all this is...?

GT: Mathematics, like I told you. Please bear with me. My point is the Catholic Church is a gigantic thing all around the world, at least compared to the ECB or the Florisota juvenile detention system.

So people hear this terrible drumbeat: "Catholic-Catholic-Catholic-Catholic..."

But if there were an ECB or a Florisota, they'd never hear "ECB-ECB-ECB" again and again—or "secular detention system in Florisota" again and again. Relative to the whole, they're too small to be noticed in the same way.

Sexual abuse of children happens everywhere. But it occurs in countless different settings. A borstal in Scotland. A nursery in Texas. A school for the disabled in Minnesota. A small congregation with a name that is much less recognisable than "Catholic." The *amount* of abuse may be similar—but it's *divided* between different institutions. That's what I mean by mathematics.

When it occurs in small, particularised, little-known settings like a Minnesota nursing home or a Scottish borstal, it's less easy to categorise. But if it happens in a vast monolithic institution like the Catholic Church, the name is on everyone's lips. Especially in our media age of sound-bites. Of course, in Ireland, the Church once ran everything. Schools, hospitals—all sorts of things. There was no "FJDS" or "ECB." It was all Catholic. So in Ireland, you just heard "Catholic-Catholic-Catholic-Catholic," because hardly anything else existed.

In fact, I had an American friend in Minnesota. He once did jury duty there. And most of the cases he heard involved sexual abuse. He told me some of the sordid, miserable details. And none of them involved the Church. They were either in the home or secular settings. Grudgingly, I admitted GT did have some kind of point. But I still wasn't sure I liked his attitude.

GPL: I hope you're not saying the Church is okay, because everyone's doing it these days—molesting children.

GT: The human side of the Church is guilty of evil. If four percent of priests in Ireland were involved in any sort of abuse, it's terrible. The cover up is just as sick as well—even if, thirty years ago, we didn't know what we know today about paedophilia or, better, ephebophilia. People did genuinely think it was curable. Still, it's no excuse. What motivated the cover-ups was not curing the priests, but shame. Priests and bishops cared more about saving face than about young people's lives. So they covered up the paedophilia or ephebophilia.

GPL: Ephebophilia—what's that?

GT: Well, it's the more accurate term. It refers to abuse of adolescents, rather than children. Most often, teenage boys. That's what it was most of the time in Ireland. It's no less sickening, of course.

We have sinned. We have *hurt* the young. Innocent lives have been ruined. And we cared more about preserving our reputation than about them. *Nostra culpa. Nostra culpa. Nostra maxima culpa.*

GPL: Well, it's good to hear you say this. I'm glad you say it's not just the media.

GT: Reality is a complex thing. I won't deny the media has exploited the situation to its own ends.

Look, GPL, you want me to be straight with you, I think. From where I'm sitting, there's clearly a New World Order that wants to destroy the Church and institute the New Secular Religion. The media is the greatest tool it has. I refuse to whitewash all this. Playing along with it, pretending the media is innocent, certainly isn't going to help those children who suffered.

It's very difficult to talk about this properly. A small percentage of Catholic priests, men who should never have been priests, have committed dreadful evil. That's a fact. But it doesn't automatically imply the media is pure and noble, either. We shouldn't forget the other ninety-six percent of priests who are innocent, but now live in fear of a witch-hunt.

The numbers are similar in secular settings—my hypothetical FJDS, for example—but it never results in a witch-hunt against the secular world. Secular morality has led to our incredibly sexualised society. It's not just pornography. All kinds of things are now eroticised. All these things certainly increase the threat to children. Nobody's innocent here.

GPL: Okay. You're right. Obviously, the situation is tremendously complicated. Media sound-bites don't help. Still, I'm glad you don't deny your Church has a real problem.

GT: I cannot deny it. As a Catholic, I aspire to place truth above all things.

GPL: There's something I just don't get, GT. You confess your Church is afflicted by evil. How on earth, then, can you hold it up like this—like it's some sort of ideal solution for humanity?!

GT: I don't. Because there is no ideal solution for humanity. Not in this world, anyway. Nothing in this fallen world is ever perfect. Undoubtedly, certain manifestations of the Church have been downright perverse.

GPL: Yes! Exactly! That's what I think. That's why I just don't get you! Just what am I missing here?

"What are you missing here? What are you missing here?" GT repeated the question slowly, deliberately, almost to himself, as if he needed to turn it over in his mind. Maybe he was also giving me a breather to calm down.

GT: Look, GPL, it would be lying to deny the evil Catholics have committed. But I would be less than honest if I didn't admit something. Frankly, *the only hope I have for humanity is the Church*. Especially at this critical hour. It would be less easy to make that claim, if anything else had a better track record. But, looking at history closely, I can't see it does.

GPL: Whoa! That's some claim you're making there.

GT: Is it? Look, GPL, we've spent some important time considering the dark side of the Church. But there's another side, too. People buried in your secular media rarely see that. Can you spare me a few moments to say something about that?

GPL: Go on then.

GT: Thank you. Let me start by reminding you that the Catholic Church has more than a billion baptised members. That is, approximately one-sixth of humanity. That's the greatest single body of any organised religion in the world. Over half the world's Christians are Catholic. There are 400,000 priests and 700,000 religious nuns and monks across the planet. There are tens of thousands of Catholic institutions, too: hospitals, orphanages, schools, dispensaries, leprosaries, shelters, soup kitchens, etc. Never in the history of humanity has so much been done by a single institution. The Church has literally clothed, fed and healed millions upon millions of people...

GPL: You're right. It's impressive.

GT: But, of course, our sensationalist media isn't interested in that. In Ireland, maybe four percent of priests committed some kind of abuse. A few of those were brutal serial rapists. They're the ones who got the media attention—not the Irish missionaries feeding the hungry in developing countries. Alas, that famous line from Shakespeare's *Julius Caesar* comes to mind.

GPL: I think I know the one you mean: "The evil that men do lives after them. The good is oft interred with their bones."

GT: Yes, the material good *alone* is incalculable. Still, one shouldn't be too materialistic here.

GPL: Materialistic? I'm not with you...

GT: Well, these days, there's a danger of only seeing the material side of things. All the feeding, medical attention, harbouring the homeless, etc. Those used to be called the *Corporal Works of Mercy.* And, obviously, they're tremendously important. However, I didn't even mention the *Spiritual Works of Mercy.* Like praying for the living and the dead. Naturally, the greatest act of mercy is the Holy Mass. I said there were four hundred thousand priests on the planet. The majority of them say Mass at least once every day. Hundreds of thousands of times a day then, His Body and Blood are given to the world. The graces that flow from that are *inconceivable.* They completely dwarf anything else the Church does for people in terms of healing and feeding their bodies.

GT looked over to his Crucifix. He bowed his head. And in a low voice he said, "Words fail, words fail utterly for this. Yet words are necessary. Everywhere people are being blinded to the stupendous reality here."

Some moments passed. I hardly knew what to say. Finally, I ventured, "Well, I can't comment on your Spiritual Works of Mercy but I've been to Africa. I see what the Catholic Church is doing there. It's a lot. And you're right: the media barely notices it. People probably are looking at Catholicism in a superficial light, myself included."

GT: Thank you, GPL. It's a major problem. Few people bother to really examine matters closely. Instead, they just regurgitate clichés, media sound-bites. For example, there's a major cliché that's been doing the rounds for years now: "Religion is the source of all wars and atrocities." You actually hear otherwise intelligent people spouting that sort of rubbish these days...

GPL: I thought you said "All conflict is ultimately theological"!

GT: I did—but that's not what people mean when they regurgitate these idiocies! They genuinely think *religious institutions*—the world's traditional, organised religions— are the source of the problem! It would be funny, if it weren't so heartbreaking. Alas, they fail to account for all the wars, massacres and atrocities that have *nothing* to do with institutions like the Church. Let's see if we can count, shall we?

With that, GT put out a hand and started lifting his fingers, one by one.

GT: World War II. Power-seeking megalomaniac, Hitler, seeks to "ethnically cleanse" Europe of the Jewish people and establish a "thousand-year Reich" for the "master race." There's no religion there—at least not in the sense critics mean it when they blame religion "for all wars."

World War I. The capitalist empire-building aspirations of several European nations were mutually threatened. So they kill each other in the trenches, with bayonets and bombs and poison gas. Again, the slaughter of the Somme, Verdun... No organised religion there, either.

The Killing Fields in Cambodia. Pol Pot tried to emulate Stalinist Marxism. Maybe three million killed.

Of course, he didn't even come close to Stalin in Russia. Twenty million dead. How many more went to the gulags, we don't know.

Oh, and don't forget Mao. Fifty million killed in China for opposing the Revolution. Or even being suspected of opposing it.

All that was just in the last century. By most accounts, the Twentieth Century was the least religious of all centuries—but it was the most genocidal by far.

If you like, we can go back further. The European settlers in the New World massacred the aboriginals because they wanted their wealth and land—not because of religion! None of these things are religious wars in the conventional sense. Shall I continue?

**GPL:** It's enough. You've made your point.

**GT:** And yet all kinds of people will actually tell you: "Religion is the cause of war and violence—Christianity especially." It's incredible. Totally incredible.

What are you missing, you ask me? Several things, perhaps. But here's one. You're missing just what these people are missing. Namely this: vast collectives everywhere have immense blood on their hands. Some of those collectives are traditional religions. The Catholic religion. The Islamic Religion. The Hindu religion. But many aren't. Capitalist empires like America's or the old British empire, for example. Or things like Russian or Chinese communism. Often, all it takes is a few monsters. In Nazi Germany, the vast majority of people weren't monsters. But often, they were too weak to stand up to the monsters...

As I say, the Catholic Church is also an immense collective. There are 1.2 billion members of the Church on this planet. Many of them are also very, very weak and, inevitably, a small number are downright perverse, sick, twisted. Evil.

What you asked me earlier about nuclear warheads is most apropos here, I think.

GPL: Asked you...?

GT: "What kind of sane creature ends up spending billions of dollars building ICBMs—nuclear warheads?" Those were your precise words, I believe.

The answer, of course, is no sane species. There's no getting around Original Sin. There are people very, very angry at the Church right now. They blame the Church. But they don't blame the Fall.

In other words: *separation from God*. One needs to take the big picture into account. If you deny the human heart is fallen, corrupted by sin, then you may never realise that *any* huge collectivity of people inevitably generates terrible deeds, at least sometimes. On the other hand, if all you have is this nice, happy New Age picture of human nature, you're bound to scapegoat.

GPL: Scapegoat?

GT: Sadly, yes. If you don't recognise sin in your own heart, you project it outside yourself. In a worldview without Original Sin, it's necessary to invent all kinds of scapegoats. Your parents mess you up. Your school messes you up. Society messes you up. Patriarchy messes you up. Religion messes you up. Back in the '60s, the scapegoat was the so-called "Establishment."

GPL: "Don't trust anyone over thirty..."

GT: That's right. The '60s youth scapegoated the older generation. *They're* the ones responsible for the mess we're in. Alas, that generation has done no better than the previous ones. Personally, I think it's done worse. Rising crime, suicide, mental illness, drug addiction, sex addiction, hedonistic consumerism on every front, as well as unbridled egocentricity. The climate going berserk. Wars everywhere around the planet still.

GPL: Phew!

GT: What are you missing here? All the above, maybe. I admit the Church can certainly manifest in perverse ways, sometimes. But Western society *without the Church* would be far more perverse.

GPL: Wow... I see now why people like Al don't like you.

GT: It's just my personal opinion, of course. There are vast matters here, which only God can judge. But I'm losing my point. If the '60s youth had recognised Original Sin, they would never have scapegoated the Establishment.

GPL: Have you ever thought you might be scapegoating the '60s?

GT: I do ask myself that. Perhaps I am. Being gentle, being fair—it's hard sweat getting it right. Heaven knows I fail. *Munda cor meum ac labia mea, omnipotens Deus.*[1]

Still, if the '60s generation had a working concept of Original Sin, I think things would have been different. Alas, the concept of Original Sin had been destroyed by that time in secular societies.

Like I said, the process begins earlier. The Eighteenth Century Enlightenment, 1789, and all that.

GPL: Yes, I see, Rousseau...

GT: He's a key figure, certainly. But there are plenty more. Voltaire, Locke, Hume can't be exonerated either. The essential point is that thousands of years of Judaeo-Christian tradition were simply jettisoned. But we can't afford to dump Original Sin. The consequences are catastrophic. Confessing Original Sin, moreover, gives people a measure of humility. If the '60s generation had more humility, they would never have tried to reinvent the wheel like they did. But perhaps you're right. I'm scapegoating them. I do get grumpy, sometimes. *Mea culpa.*

Anyway, would you like a root beer?

"A what?" I asked, slightly jarred by the transition. For the last half hour he'd been thundering about cultural decadence. Suddenly, he was smiling and cheery again.

---

[1] Cleanse my heart and my lips, O Almighty God (from the Tridentine Latin Mass).

GT: Root beer! It's a sickly, sweet American drink. Snoopy the dog drinks it—at least when he's the famous World War One fighter pilot. Most people this side of the pond can't stand the stuff—say it tastes like medicine. Or mouth wash. But you're welcome to try some.

GPL: Er, no thanks. I'll pass, this time.

GT: Well, you won't mind if I partake, then? I can't handle the real stuff anymore.

GPL: No?

GT: Makes me less gentle. As you can see, I have to watch my grumpiness. But you, my good man, are most welcome, if you wish. I have a can of Guinness somewhere.

GPL: Well, thank you, GT, I'd like that.

Privately, I couldn't help but notice the incongruity here. He was supposed to be a traditionalist, wasn't he? Not endorsing artificial sugared drinks by the giant American corporations he said were destroying Irish culture.

"You're right about my incongruities," he said after a moment. "I can't help it—I developed a fondness for it in Tombstone, Arizona, back before the gunfight at the O.K. Corral. Anyway, I'm a Catholic, not a Puritan. Moderation is the key here. You'll see I'm full of little contradictions. Ralph Waldo Emerson said it best I think." And with that, he poured out the drinks, a tankard of Guinness for me and one with root beer for himself.

GPL: Emerson?

GT: "A foolish consistency is the hobgoblin of little minds." Cheers. Let's talk about important stuff.

GPL: Okay, I hear you, GT. Clearly, the global situation is extremely complex. Obviously, evil isn't confined to the Catholic Church. Maybe it's simplistic to think Christianity has lost all credibility now. But I can't help thinking you're being too simplistic, yourself.

GT: I probably am. But I'd be careful with that liberal trope, if I were you.

GPL: What—?

GT: Suggesting a person is simplistic, unnuanced, polarising, extremist, etc. Obviously, sometimes it's true. Other times it's intellectual trickery to ridicule something people don't like. They call something unsophisticated, when, really, they're just too cynical or lazy to face the unpleasant truths of modernity. If you dare to suggest the past was better in any way, they call you naive or nostalgic. Beware of intellectual cynicism! Too often, it paralyses the will to work for something better.

Still, you think I'm wrong to label everything in terms of cultural decay.

GPL: You took the words right out of my mouth! Like I said before, good things happened in the '60s, too!

GT: Yes, they did. I promised we'd come back to that. I don't deny any sort of progress. There have been some gains, admittedly. We don't have racial segregation like we did in Alabama or South Africa. Racial tensions have eased a little. We're clearer about certain human rights now. Women have achieved certain rights over the last centuries. Property rights, voting rights, other important things, too. The angels rejoice at these things, you know.

GPL: It's a relief to hear you say that!

GT: Still, I don't know if women are more free today than they were. Most of us—men and women—are less free, I think. Women face a different form of tyranny now. Like the tyranny of being sex objects for male gratification. I don't just mean the vast increase in pornography and prostitution, phone sex, things like that. I also mean supposedly "normal" things. Like fashion, make-up, the pressure to have a certain body type. It's all very well for the capitalists behind the cosmetics industry—but it places women in bondage. And here's another thing: women are bound into capitalist wage slavery like never before. And certainly a woman is less free to walk the streets than she was before our crime-saturated society.

No doubt the angels weep for women today. And who

knows where all this is headed in the future, if we keep going down the same path?

The French have a saying, "Plus ça change, plus c'est la même chose."

**GPL:** The more things change, the more they stay the same.

**GT:** Yes, indeed. The New Secular Religion loves to proclaim its "progress." Too often, however, it's more like "six of one, half a dozen of the other."

It's a pity we can't consult the angels as they monitor human history. Would they tell us—overall—that women have made progress? I can't say I know the answer to that one.

**GPL:** I'd like to hear you tell that to a feminist…

**GT:** It doesn't square with the prevailing secular dogmas, I know. All we ever hear these days is how bad the past was.

Here in Ireland, people speak of the old Catholic culture as nothing but humbug, hypocrisy. And, of course, there *was* hypocrisy. I don't deny that. There always is.

Alas, contemporary society can't see its own shadow. The modern, liberal world: so critical of the evils of the past, yet so reluctant to criticise its own evils. There's hypocrisy for you.

The problem with the New Secular Religion is that it's *triumphalist*. It's forever trumpeting a simplistic narrative of progress that doesn't recognise its own failures. The end result is self-righteousness: "holier than thou." But you can't always be patting yourself on the back for "progress." It wears thin after a while.

**GPL:** Whew…! Now, I really, really see why Al called you a dinosaur!

**GT:** Well, I refuse to join in the great secular song of "progress" and "tolerance." That's all. I see that hypocrisy exists in every age. Catholic Ireland could be hypocritical. No doubt about it. But we're kidding ourselves if we think we're doing better today.

Here's another example. Once upon a time, the Europeans went to the New World and massacred the indigenous peoples. These days there's genuine horror for the "sins of the fathers" in places like America and Australia. But today there's full-blown massacre of the unborn, instead.

Now, today's abortionists don't believe they're doing anything wrong. Neither did those who exterminated the aboriginals! At the time, they had all sorts of justifications. Alas, often one only recognises evil in hindsight. It will be the same with abortion. One day, there will be penance on a massive scale for what we've done to our unborn babies.

GPL: Whew and double whew!

GT: What I'm saying isn't popular. That's for sure. Christianity isn't meant to be popular. But I can't help it. I agree with Mr Lennon and you: "The world is so wrong." There's no room for complacency. And it's not always easy being gentle when you realise how much people suffer every day under our secular regime.

For a few moments, we both sat in silence. It had stopped snowing outside and the sun was shining through the window. I stared at the fire whilst GT stoked it. For all our obvious conflict, I couldn't help but feel a sneaking regard for him. He obviously meant it when he talked about human suffering. I realised I felt something extraordinarily peaceful sitting in that room. I finished my Guinness with pleasure.

"I'm all out of Guinness," he said. "Sure you won't have a root beer?"

"Quite sure," I replied.

"Well, forgive me, I do get thirsty from all my jabbering." And with that, he poured himself another.

# X

# Traditio et Ratio

AFTER he downed his root beer, GT looked at me and said, "I realise, of course, that we're far from finished with your objections to my religion. Nor mine to yours. There are plenty more important disagreements. Our male priesthood, for instance. Our stance on artificial contraception, homosexual acts—to name only a few."

He was right, of course, and I told him so.

"Well, most of this is not simply a Catholic thing," GT continued. "We're back to those magical 1960s where—poof!—everything that had been wrong before suddenly wasn't. Before then, the West had certain traditional rules about sexual conduct. Let's see if we can name them."

With that, he began counting out his "rules" on his fingers.

GT: 1. *No pornography.* Sexuality is something beautiful to be shared in the intimate commitment between man and woman. A woman is not a commodity to be bought and sold for men's gratification.

2. *No prostitution.* Same principle, again.

3. *No divorce.* Admittedly divorce was legal in Protestant countries (unlike Catholic countries, such as Italy, Spain or Ireland, where it wasn't). Still, no-fault divorce was unheard of and the rates for divorce were far lower than they are today. Marriage was still considered sacred, especially in cultures where marriage is a Sacrament and not just a human-made "contract" between consenting parties. In other words: *a sacred mystery.* "What God has joined together, let no man put asunder."

4. *No adultery.* Sexuality entails loyalty, fidelity to one's spouse, but also, of course, to any children who may be born from that sacred union in marriage.

5. *No fornication.* The beauty of marriage again. This likewise extends love to children. The catastrophe of one parent families was far less likely in the past, if not altogether eliminated. Today, we have no idea what we are doing to our children's psyches…

6. *No abortion.* This used to be a "no-brainer" everywhere —to employ the contemporary vernacular. Christians, Hindus, Buddhists—it horrified everyone alike.

7. *No artificial contraception.* It wasn't just Catholics who held to this, but all Christians. Right up to the 1950s, Protestants, too, had alarm bells about contraception. This one is harder for rationalist, materialistic minds to comprehend. They don't understand the holistic nature of sex.

8. *No masturbation.* Where the erotic imagination is necessarily stimulated and sexuality is reduced to mere pleasure.

9. *No homosexual acts.* This was yet another "no-brainer" —in every religion. It was obvious from Natural Law that sexual intercourse was divinely intended for man and woman. (And Natural Law isn't simply a Christian understanding. It was revered in Islam and other religions, too. It goes back to Plato and Aristotle, at least.)

10. *No polygamy.* Western society still tends to believe in this one. But, the way things are going, it won't be long before it's accepted like the rest.

I've run out of fingers. Still, there are more things that used to be unacceptable, which may not be in the future. Sadomasochism. Incest. Bestiality. Necrophilia…

GPL: Whoa! I understand certain things you mention. Some of them seem reasonable to me—but not others.

GT: "Reasonable"… hmm. Interesting word, that. And very telling! *"Reasonable to you"* is even more telling. Therein lies the great difference.

**GPL:** Great difference between what? Your religion and "mine"—so-called?

**GT:** More or less, yes. My religion includes Natural Law as well as tradition, which, in turn, depends on revelation. Yours is restricted to reason alone. (Or, at least, what *it* understands by reason—which is purely human reason.)

That's basically what rationalism means: *human reason alone.*

For Catholics, rationalism has always been suspect. According to pure rationalism, if there's *no demonstrable reason* three people shouldn't marry, they ought to have the right. Or four. Or sixteen for that matter. It's the same principle elsewhere. For example, if you can't demonstrate human reasons why people should abstain from masturbation, it's okay.

Again, Christianity rejects that. It looks toward something higher than reason alone.

**GPL:** Well, maybe that's why people say Catholicism is irrational. Didn't your people try to burn Galileo?

**GT:** No. But, tragically, they did imprison him. *Nostra culpa.* Countless Catholics, of course, have been appallingly irrational. Still, that's not the same as saying Catholicism itself is irrational.

The Church always aspires to reason. God established reason. In that sense, God is supremely rational. But God isn't limited to reasons we humans understand—in other words: rationalism. God is rational, yes, but he transcends rationalism.

You could also say God is both rational and trans-rational or meta-rational, even. The Church likewise aspires to the same. Again, that's the great difference between your religion and mine.

I was beginning to understand how GT's mind operated. Even if I didn't know as much European philosophy as he, I was blessed with a decent education. Clearly, GT was tracing all this back to the Eighteenth Century again—the Age of Reason.

GPL: I suppose you'll tell me "my religion" is based on Enlightenment rationalism. 1789 and all that again?

GT: Yes, 1789 and all that. Pumped up by the '60s revolution. Anything that transcends human reason gets excluded. And since God always transcends human reason, God is marginalised. Divine Law also transcends purely human reason. That gets excluded too. Which is a pity if God really does exist and Divine Law does too.

GPL: Yes, I begin to see. If divine supra-human laws really *do* exist, then what you're saying makes sense. Some kind of sense, anyway.

GT: And if God doesn't exist, then it makes no sense. None whatsoever. It's that simple. We may as well adopt rationalism. Everything depends on whether you take God seriously or not.

Obviously, they didn't take God seriously in 1789 and we see the consequences today. The West has been in conflict ever since—between those who take God and godly law seriously—and those who don't.

GPL: You and Anna versus Al and me...

GT: I'm afraid so. Revolution and Counter-Revolution.

I glanced at his odd Irish tricolour again. "That flag, your Carlist officer, that book you have about the multinational army defending Rome against Italian annexation..." I mused out loud.

GT: Yes, in the past, the division was much sharper, clearer. Not fuzzy. Catholics knew history better. Now, everyone's trying to Be Nice. It doesn't help, if you ask me.

As a Christian, I trust in a Divine Law that decrees the sexual act is sacred, reserved to a man and a women who are committed to each other in the deepest intimacy. That means that homosexual acts, masturbatory acts, fornicatory acts, adulterous acts are deviations from the sacred ideal.

What we call sin is *hamartia* in the Greek of the New Testament. It means "not hitting the target." Again, they're deviations. That doesn't mean the Church condemns the people who commit these acts. Only God can judge a man's soul. The Church, however, *does* say that all those sexual acts fail to hit God's target. Likewise with divorce...

GPL: I don't know what to say, GT. I mean, no divorce?! People have a right to end their marriage if it's not—

GT: What is a right? You can't have a right to do a wrong. There's no right to lie, to cheat, to steal, to abort... Why should divorce—trying to destroy God's sacrament—be any different?

GPL: This is just inconceivable in our day and age!

GT: Yes, to the modern, globalised mind. But not very long ago in Ireland, it was the democratic will of the majority.

GPL: Really?

GT: In 1937, the Irish people voted for a constitution which forbad divorce. Then in 1986, there was a referendum here to permit divorce. Divorce was defeated again—by a margin of two to one. Another 1995 referendum allowed it in only by the narrowest of margins—9,114 votes in a country of four million. Virtually, fifty percent of the people still voted "no." Now, by 1995, Ireland was awash in aggressive, well-funded secular propaganda like never before. The masters of the New World Order decreed that Ireland simply *had* to have divorce. Without their help, divorce would undoubtedly have been defeated again.

GPL: Wow...

GT: I take it you're amazed by what I'm saying?

GPL: Frankly, yes.

GT: I'll be frank with you, too, GPL. From where I'm standing, that sort of amazement is just another sign of your creed. Divorce is like sacred dogma for the New Secular Religion. The fact that Ireland once honoured Divine Law above permissiveness is incomprehensible to the secular mindset. Yet right up to 1995, this country still resisted the 1789 brigade.

GPL: I am amazed—like you say. I mean all this "Divine Law" jazz. Even if it does exist, how would we ever know? Something like that is easily abused, to say the least!

GT: We know through wrestling—constantly—with Faith, Reason and Natural Law. Obviously, a tremendous capacity for abuse exists. But don't kid yourself that 1789 hasn't led to tremendous abuse either! Our crass, materialistic society is the result.

GT: I can't believe what I'm hearing! You're talking about some kind of theocracy!

GT: Ireland, I remind you, was a democracy. Instead of the New Secular Religion, it once chose Christianity instead.

GPL: You mean Catholicism!

GT: Not necessarily. For example, in 1937 the small Anglican confession in Ireland also supported the divorce clause in the Constitution. And de Valera framed that constitution so that Ireland wasn't a Catholic state like Spain or Portugal. The Church actually accused Dev of being too liberal!

GPL: Unbelievable! What about minorities? What about non-believers?

GT: That's an important question. Non-believers, for example, must be respected. Respect, however, means clear thinking and hard work to find solutions which are just. It doesn't mean *caving into their every demand*. Once you end up trying to please every single minority, you're left with the lowest common denominator everyone can agree with. That's low. Very low. Too low! A majority of believers can be cowed into remaking society to fit the vision of the minority. Alas, that's what happened in Ireland.

GPL: You can also ask where all this is going in the future. Today we're seeing tyranny by a growing minority of militant secularists and atheists who end up—successfully!—demanding the system reflect their values. Over in your country, local government was talking about renaming Christmas "Winterval." That's a clear example of a small minority calling the shots. Admittedly, it hasn't been legislated... *yet*. Still, it's a clear indication of where things are headed. Your Political Correctness is running riot.

GPL: It's not *"my"* Political Correctness!

GT: Isn't it? If you study the phenomenon, I think you'll see a direct progression from the secular principles you uphold. Too often, it's a means to control the majority by a small militant minority.

GT stood up and walked over to his bookcases. "Let me return to Ireland. Perhaps you think I'm harping on about this island— harping on my Irish harp, you could say," he said smiling. "But, again, Ireland represents, in microcosm, what happened across the West: the transition from Christendom to secular capitalism."

"My point about de Valera," he continued, "is that Dev believed wholeheartedly in liberal, democratic principles. These days, there's a common, dangerous notion that liberal democracy and Christian society are incompatible. Dev proved that wasn't true. Allow me to read you something..."

Grumpily, I nodded and GT pulled a volume from the shelf. "This isn't from de Valera. It's by the Catholic political thinker, Valentin Tomberg. Still, Tomberg argues for the liberal minimum state—in contrast to the fascist maximum state which seeks to control culture." He opened the book and began reading:

> The liberal minimum state... must shape public life only to the degree necessary to protect... liberty...
>
> This liberty, however, may be used in certain ways: Individuals, who are citizens of a liberal legal state, may use their freedom to choose certain obligations, which for example go hand in hand with Christian religion and the Church. Then the state must serve the Church in the same way as it must serve every other use of freedom chosen by its citizens. The liberal minimum state thus becomes a *Christian minimum state*. The latter is in its meaning a legal order serving Christianity. It relates to the Church and the totality of cultural life as the body relates to the soul. As the body serves the soul by providing it the location for a developing consciousness, so the Christian minimum state serves the Christian culture, represented and led by the Church.

GT closed the book, saying, "He goes on to argue that cultural matters like education must not be determined by the State. That way leads to Fascism. Dev—and those who elected him—could appreciate arguments like that, which is why the Church ran the schools in Ireland. All this is radical today in our secular culture. But, in 1937, Irish people voted for a constitution very much along those lines. They democratically chose something else."

"And today, people are democratically choosing secularism!" I said hotly.

"Yes, indeed... although how free that choice is—given the sheer, unprecedented power of the media these days—is another question.... However, my point is that *liberal democracy and Christian society are not incompatible.* If a state achieves a Christian majority again, it can legitimately choose what Tomberg and Dev each articulated in their different ways. Christians can work for a state that protects Christian values instead of the New Secular Religion. In my opinion, we have to. The New Secular Religion is leading us to ruin. The 'Culture of Death,' as St. John Paul II called it. He didn't just mean abortion, but death on every front. Death of the soul, death of the family, death of culture, death of the environment. The final end of basing society purely on Enlightenment rationalism."

I wanted to throw up my hands and scream. But I held on, tight, to the arms of my chair—so I wouldn't hit the roof.

GPL: Okay, okay, GT! I get it: you honestly believe these medieval concepts! But look, even if I agreed with you that Enlightenment rationalism was creating a completely materialistic society—which, of course, I don't—surely there's another problem to all your archaic laws about sexual morality!

GT: Which is...?

GPL: Some of those things you condemn are pretty tough to avoid! It's cruel to impose all your rules on human nature. Under your regime, people would have no choice but to repress their basic human nature or become hypocrites trying to live up to an impossible ideal.

GT: Do I detect the voice of one of your great prophets, I wonder?

GPL: What—?

GPL: I'm talking about Freud. He's very important in your religion, I know. But if you don't mind looking at that Bible one last time, you can see what Christ would say to Freud. Matthew 5:27–30.

I indulged him once more, flipping open the Bible to the Gospel of Matthew:

> You have heard that it was said to them of old: Thou shalt not commit adultery. But I say to you, that whosoever shall look on a woman to lust after her, hath already committed adultery with her in his heart. And if thy right eye scandalise thee, pluck it out and cast it from thee. For it is expedient for thee that one of thy members should perish, rather than that thy whole body be cast into hell. And if thy right hand scandalise thee, cut it off, and cast it from thee: for it is expedient for thee that one of thy members should perish, rather than that thy whole body be cast into hell.

GT: What do you say to that?

GPL: I'm *aghast.*

GT: Do I recall you saying something about Jesus being a "great moral teacher"? You might want to rethink that. By your Freudian reckoning, Jesus must have offloaded his own neurotic guilt-complex onto billions of people these last two thousand years!

Anyway, I'm a Christian. I choose Jesus over Freud. And I don't conveniently forget Jesus, when he says tough things about sex. And, of course, they *are* tough—especially in our incredibly sexualised society. They were somewhat easier in the past, before sex bombarded us constantly in the media. They were also easier *when people still received the Holy Sacraments.* And not just Communion, but absolution: cleansing, healing absolution. Our Lord knew these things were tough. That's why he provided the Sacraments! Today, we forget that. No wonder sexual restraint seems so impossible!

Today, in our de-sacramentalised, highly sexualised culture, men lust after women like never before. I concede it may be virtually impossible for a teenage boy not to masturbate. What matters though is not perfection—that's impossible—but *honest endeavour to conform to a higher ideal*. In the past, all kinds of men tried to discipline their sexual impulses. In Ireland of old, people aspired to "hit the target" of sexual fidelity and chastity. That doesn't mean they always managed. Still, it remained an important cultural aspiration. And the Sacraments provided the strength for that. Now, people abandon themselves to sex. What was it Chesterton said? "Birth control means no birth and no control."

GPL: Like I said, I'm aghast. You're living on a completely different planet!

GT: It's the same planet, my friend. I just belong to a completely different religion. That religion reigned in much of the West, till the '60s. In Ireland, it reigned even longer. I just find rationalism incapable of engaging the sublime mysteries of sex.

GPL: What's that supposed to mean?

GT: Well, take what Christ said about "adultery of the heart." By looking at a woman with lust, a man enters into an adulterous liaison with her at a subtle level of reality. That liaison may be invited, if the woman flaunts her body. Or it may be uninvited. An innocent woman is demeaned— violated even. Again, at a subtle level.

Of course, talking about "subtle levels of reality" is nonsense to a perspective framed from pure rationalism. *Rationalism, in the end, amounts to materialism*. It's only interested in matter: the stuff you observe with your five senses. And nothing else.

But Our Lord *cared* about higher, more subtle levels of reality. That's what I mean by sublime mysteries of sex. But a culture addicted to "rational" explanations can't see that. It's not surprising you get pornography, increased divorce, abortion, prostitution, rape, sexual abuse and all the rest. Sexuality is a Sacred Mystery which can't be reduced to human terms. Christianity understands that. Rationalist materialism doesn't.

**GPL:** Phew!

**GT:** We desperately need to transcend rationalism—to honour God's reason, not ours. In the past, we depended on tradition and Natural Law for that. And not only in Christianity. Other world religions, Islam, Buddhism, Hinduism, did the same. These days people look to Eastern religions, conveniently forgetting their sexual morality is much the same as ours. Here's a double standard for you: the Dalai Lama has spoken out against homosexual acts. But the Dalai Lama is "cool" in Western culture these days. People overlook what he says about sex. Not so with the Pope! He says the same as the Dalai Lama—but he's "uncool." So people brand him a homophobe and bigot.

Or take Gandhi—again highly respected in the West today. In fact, Gandhi's sexual ethic was far stricter than Catholicism's. But we forget that, just like we forget everything else that doesn't suit us. Not only Jesus Christ, but also Gandhi, Mohammed, Buddha, Moses...

The global religious wisdom of millennia has been dispatched by the Western sexual revolutionaries of the '60s. That's quite an achievement, don't you think? Forgive me, I'm being sarcastic again.

At that point, a sharp rapping came at the door. GT went to answer it. Standing in the hallway was an African man covered from head to toe in lettuce leaves with a large wooden basin on his head.

"Greetings," the man said. "I am King Salad-Bowl of the Thousand Islands! I may not look European, but I am really a Transylvanian royal. I also come from the eighteenth century—the year 1767, to be precise. But I'm trapped—trapped in the body of a Ugandan born in 1995! In other words, I am not only a trans-ethnic, but a *trans-temporal*. I demand full, immediate, and unconditional legal recognition for my true nature and identity! I have a petition here for other trans-ethnics, trans-temporals, and trans-vegetables. Would you like to sign it?"

"Oh, please," GT said and promptly shut the door on him.

"Of course, you realise, this means war, you time-ist pig!" King Salad-Bowl screamed from behind the door, before stomping down the stairs.

I looked around the room again, more desperate than ever to find evidence of that blasted hidden camera. But there wasn't any.

"Truly, the world is turning insane," GT said in a low, pained voice, slumping into his chair. "Alas, you can't expect anything else when you rubbish every last shred of Natural Law and global traditional wisdom. *Miserere nobis.*"

All this was simply too much for me.

GPL: I just can't buy it, GT! Your precious global tradition includes plenty that was wrong! You mentioned Gandhi. What about the caste system in India? Gandhi decried that! Isn't it possible tradition is wrong sometimes?

GT: Certainly, tradition is wrong sometimes. There's no denying that. Tradition, like everything else in this world, is fallen. It has to be continually developed. But your New Secular Religion isn't saying that. It claims tradition is wrong *every time*.

GPL: Every time?! I don't think so...

GT: Every time it disagrees with rationalism, yes. Of course, when it accords with rationalism, there's no problem. Rationalists and traditionalists both agree murder is wrong, for example.

But watch out when religion calls for anything higher than rationalism! (Not to mention Freud's Pleasure Principle.) Then, religion is thrown out the window. Every time.

GPL: Some would say your Church does just the opposite: throwing reason out the window, every time.

GT: Some would say that, yes. Alas, that might be true of certain Christian fundamentalists. But Catholicism has nothing to do with that. The Church teaches *fides et ratio*. Faith and reason are both needed. Faith without reason becomes fideism and superstition. Reason without faith leads to our present nihilist wasteland.

No. The Church calls us to confront reality. Not just mindlessly exclude millennia of traditional wisdom simply because it doesn't jibe with "1968." It's not easy grappling with reason and tradition—but it leads to better results.

You mentioned the caste system. That's a good example of what I mean. Gandhi went on a long hunger strike against caste and nearly died. But it changed the face of India forever. Caste couldn't be eliminated overnight, of course, but caste has never been the same again, since Gandhi.

Yet Gandhi was also profoundly traditional. Think of him and his spinning wheel, abandoning Western clothes. Again, Gandhi's sexual ethic alone would be attacked right, left and centre today. Gandhi was no rationalist revolutionary. He engaged tradition. Only by engaging it could he change it.

**GPL:** Yes, I see that...

**GT:** Tradition is alive. It develops. It grows. It wouldn't be tradition otherwise, just Pharisaism—the dead letter of the law. Jesus resembled Gandhi in that: profoundly traditional, but willing to challenge tradition, too... but it goes without saying that Our Lord Jesus Christ stands on a summit infinitely more exalted than Gandhi or any other fallen human being.

Still, the principle remains the same. Tradition develops by dint of the saints and geniuses who engage with it. Not by those who reject it. And certainly not by the latest fad!

I only mention Gandhi because you've heard of him. I could have invoked any number of great Catholic saints—but no-one ever hears about them in modern English society. Your education and media have seen to that.

I nodded, annoyed by his anti-English tone again. I was also irritated by something in the background: strange muttering noises. But I couldn't tell where they came from. Then, once again, GT picked up on my thoughts.

**GT:** I'm certainly not saying the Anglosphere is the source of our troubles. I *am* saying it's the dominant culture on our planet, with enormous influence. Inevitably, both the good things it stands for and the bad affect everything else.

The strange mutterings had become louder. I could even make out some words and phrases now. "Appalling, absolutely appalling... Superstitious nonsense... Crackpot... Lunatic theocracy... We'll have to see to this... Exterminate it." I realised it was coming from the landing outside. I looked over to the door. The cat was there, arching his back and hissing. "There's someone out there," I said to GT.

"Yes, I know," he sighed. "It's Professor Rigid Dorkins, unfortunately. He's a sociobiologist. Wrote a book called *Selfish Jeans* or something like that. To me, it looks like Social Darwinism, although he denies that. Still, it's undoubtedly fuelled our new egocentric society. Alas, we'd better let him in."

And with that he cried out, "Come on in, Dr Dorkins. No sense muttering to yourself in the dark like that."

And with that, a sour-faced, aging English gentleman came striding through the door...

RD: Trying to propagate your evil religion again?

GT: Evidently, you mean my Catholicism.

RD: I've said it before. I don't mind doing so again. Second most evil religion on the planet after Islam.

I heard all those traditional rules of yours. One or two might be reasonable. The rest are pure nonsense. There's absolutely no evidence that masturbation, homosexual intercourse, sex outside marriage are harmful to anyone.

GT: Like there's no evidence a foetus has a human soul...

RD: There's no evidence *anything* has a human soul.

GT: It follows, then, that law shouldn't take account of the human soul.

RD: Of course not.

GT: Some of us would say that leads inevitably to a completely soulless society.

RD: Society, of course, has no soul either. These are just sentimental feelings—like all religion. It's a virus of the mind.

People blindly following something for which there is no evidence whatsoever.

GT: What you mean, Dr Dorkins, is *scientific* evidence—demonstrable by reason or empirical observation.

RD: No other kind of evidence exists, you old fool. Everything must be based on evidence.

GT: But that statement itself is not based on evidence!

Only your *faith* declares everything must be based on evidence. It then dictates what constitutes that evidence. Everything else gets screened out. The universe becomes restricted to your own materialist metaphysic.

One never gets away from faith. "All conflict is ultimately theological." The faith of scientism versus traditional faith.

But, really, I'm not sure there's the least point in exchanging these views. I see no possible bridge between our two faiths...particularly as you won't even admit to having a faith.

RD: Ludicrous, as ever. I can't say I enjoy our conversations either. But dangerous people like you must be exposed. According to your fascist rules, we should all be living miserable sexually repressed lives and condemning homosexuals to hell. Or anyone else who doesn't fit into your twisted religion.

GT sighed, "I never said any such thing, of course."

GT appeared different now: listless, largely silent. Had he wanted to, he could have easily debated the professor. Indeed, Dorkins was badgering the old man to defend himself. But GT only ventured the odd word or two, sticking to his guns that Dorkins, too, possessed a faith, which he denied. Once, when Dorkins was getting worked up about "theocracy," GT objected to his "seculocracy." Yet for the most part GT listened politely. Still, his attention seemed elsewhere, beyond the professor's horizons. At times, GT winced in pain, even grimaced. I couldn't help feeling it wasn't just Dorkins, but that something else plagued the old man.

I felt helpless. Like GT, I suspect, I saw this conversation was going nowhere. I even started feeling sorry for the old man.

There was something brittle, ruthless about our visitor, even inquisitorial.

Finally, I decided to chip in. "I don't agree with GT's religion," I said. "But still, there's a core point he's making. There may be something higher to the universe than science can see. That something may even possess higher laws. If a foetus does have a soul, for instance, it follows that it has a right to life. Everything depends on…"

Dorkins interrupted me: "If fairies at the bottom of the garden exist, it follows they have rights, too!"

And with that he started ridiculing us both. It went on, relentlessly. Clearly, he had no interest in dialogue of any kind. At one point he talked about arresting the Pope as an "enemy of humanity" and called Vatican City a "crackpot, heartless theocracy" established by Mussolini. Even I recognised his historical slurs. The Italian state had conquered and annexed the Vatican by brute force. It didn't establish it. Only later on did Mussolini's government return a tiny postage-stamp-size piece of land from all the territory Italy had seized. This was the true origin of the vastly-reduced Vatican state that Dorkins claimed Mussolini had founded. Dorkins said more like that: slanted and misleading, to say the least. But I'm not recording it all here. Frankly, it was pretty ugly and I'd rather not fill these pages with ugliness. All the while, GT said little or nothing.

At last, the old man spoke. "This has gone on long enough. You're demanding that we base an entire society solely on scientific materialism, dispensing with every traditional form of morality that doesn't agree with your marginalisation of the transcendent. Massacring the unborn is only the beginning of what you have in mind. Excuse me, there is something I must now do."

With that, GT rose from his chair, lifting his right hand with that wild ring of his. Very slowly and deliberately, he started tracing the sign of the cross in front of Dorkins. Meanwhile, he prayed in a low voice, starting with: *"In nomine Patris et Filii et Spiritus Sancti."* The effect was startling. GT was a big man, but he seemed even taller than before. It was as though I saw his full stature only now and he'd grown half a foot in height. Certainly, his presence filled the room and his eyes brimmed with stern, luminous intensity.

"More of your mumbo jumbo, magic spells in medieval Latin," Dorkins sneered.

GT simply continued speaking Latin in his low voice, whilst making the sign of the Cross in all directions. Then he lifted his arm straight out so that the ring pointed directly to the professor's heart.

"Oh I get it! You can't say anything intelligent, so you're going to zap me with your magic ring, are you?" he scoffed. "Say something to defend yourself, you old fool, defend your ridiculous religion."

But the Latin only continued. And as GT stood there, the stone of the ring, I swear, appeared to change colour, glowing a deeper fiery red. It even seemed to emit a steady beam of light. I glanced at the window. The afternoon sun hung low in the northern February sky. Its rays fell directly on GT and his ring. Obviously, it was all a trick of the light. Still, the effect was unforgettable.

Abruptly, Dorkins started shrieking, hurling insults. But somehow his screeching became more and more plaintive, pitiful even. It was as though the energy were being sucked out of him. He started to look smaller, bent over, frail, like a poor, old man.

"Ridiculous," he protested. By now, his voice was almost a croak. With that, he made for the door. I thought he might slam it. But even pulling it open seemed like an effort for him and he slunk out without saying another word.

> GPL: If I didn't know better, I'd say you did something to that man! Admittedly, he wasn't very pleasant. But you weren't exactly gentle with him, either.

> GT: I said I was gentle; I didn't say I was a milksop! I didn't say I wouldn't defend innocent children.

> GPL: Children?

> GT: That man is writing stuff that cages the human imagination—for centuries perhaps. Parents, educators will hand it on to the next generation. And they'll hand it on to the one after that. The children—trapped in a nihilistic universe

stripped of meaning. No grace, no purpose. Innocent children ravaged by monsters…

GPL: You're calling him a monster?!

GT: Not him, poor, miserable fellow. Still, monstrous forces are operating through him. He has a brilliant, rational intellect, adept at creating highly plausible "explanations." Demons can utilise minds like his.

But in case you're wondering, I never did anything to that wretched, old man. Only the spirit working through him. It's a very powerful, angry, violent spirit. My ring only works on demons. Alas, if someone spends their entire waking life animated by a spirit like that, there's nothing left to turn to when that spirit is exhausted.

If I'd kept going, I might have liberated him. But it was too dangerous: It could have been too much for him to bear. He might've died. It's unspeakably tragic what's happened to him—and so many others these days.

"Tragic, tragic," he repeated. "Can you imagine the world in fifty years, if present trends continue…?"

And with that he sat down in his chair, buried his face in his hands and wept. Heavy sobs shook his massive frame. I just sat there, dumbstruck. For the longest time, I had no idea what to say. GT gradually stopped weeping and stared at me, with horror in his eyes.

GT: It's the same with the global capitalists. With the help of modern technology, they're constructing the most effective cages ever made for the human imagination. A child grows up from its earliest years with their messages implanted firmly in its heart. But the problem is greater than simply the new materialists, the new atheists.

A spectre of materialism is haunting the world. That spectre assumes many forms: atheism, consumerism, capitalism, utilitarianism, functionalism, determinism, psychologism. Indeed, reductionism of any sort…

You see why I'm a traditionalist. I can see no viable future for humanity based on science alone, reason alone. It's simply not enough to prevent our continued downward spiral into greed and perversity. The rationalism of previous centuries is leading us to the Wasteland—where everything sacred is obliterated.

Then, suddenly, GT looked up with horror on his face. "Good heavens, there's been a breach!"

"A breach?"

"It's too complicated to explain. The forces pouring through that poor man were more powerful than I realised! The field in this room has been compromised. I never expected that!"

GT leapt from his chair. "You must forgive me. The breach will only take twenty minutes to repair. But it must be done immediately. You can stay there, if you like. There's been plenty today to chew over and I think you'll find the nature of the operation conducive to meditation."

With that, GT began "repairing the breach." He knelt, facing east and praying, once more, in Latin. His prayers continued as he moved around the room, swinging the censer, filled with frankincense. Several times, GT used the ring in a deliberate, methodical fashion, tracing the sign of the Cross on the ceiling, the floor and the four walls. Repeatedly, I heard him invoke the Archangel Michael: "*Sancte Michael Archangele...*"

I watched him carefully for the first few minutes. But then, as before, the effect of his prayers was profoundly soothing. I turned our conversation over in my mind. Maybe it was good to contemplate things, as he'd suggested.

So many questions left unanswered. We still hadn't got to things like married priests or women's ordination. At least, we hadn't addressed them specifically. But perhaps it wasn't necessary: GT had already provided his answers. It was obvious what he would say: the Catholic Church couldn't surrender to purely rationalist arguments for these things. That was the way of the world since 1789. Instead, the Church was devoted to something higher than reason alone.

I recall Anna telling me the Church had no right to ordain women. Instead, her duty was to guard "the deposit of faith" entrusted to her, Anna said. With ordaining women or married men, the real issue was the Sacrament. The same was true of marriage. And the Church considered the Sacraments as transcendent mysteries far beyond ordinary human logic.

You either believed in a sacred mystery here—which meant protecting that mystery—or you didn't. It may as well be "fairies at the bottom of the garden," then. Meaning nothing, nada, zero, zilch.

It was dawning on me that *everything hinged on this*. A few years ago I had heard atheists like Dorkins calling for drugs or lobotomy to cure the "religious virus of the mind." I could see the logical consistency here. *If* all religion amounted to was mass delusion—one leading to hatred, bigotry and war—then surely the atheists had a point! Why shouldn't we try to treat it medically?

But if, on the other hand, the claims of the Catholic Church were actually true, what then? If marriage weren't just a human contract but a mystical Sacrament bestowed by God Himself, weren't Catholics obliged to protect the Sacrament? Clearly, the same principle was at stake not only for ordination and the other Sacraments—but for many other things besides: abortion, conception, sex, death...

Were there only two options, then—tradition or reason? But, no, I remembered what GT had said. Tradition might be flawed, but it could be corrected—not by fads or revolutionaries but rather by wise people who cherished tradition. Reason had a role to play here, but it mustn't annihilate tradition. These were strange, new thoughts for me. Could all GT's prayers be having an effect?

Then, I noticed GT had changed languages. He was now praying in Gaelic. I was transfixed. There was something at once solemn and majestic in the way he spoke the old Irish. One line "Atomriug indiu" was repeated over and over. It penetrated me. At the time, I didn't understand its meaning, of course. Later, I discovered an old book from 1898 where I read it meant "I arise today" and came from *The Deer's Cry*, attributed to St. Patrick. (A portion of which is known as St. Patrick's Breastplate.) The book also said:

> Patrick made this hymn; in the time of Loegaire mac Neill,
> it was made, and the cause of its composition was for the

protection of himself and his monks against deadly enemies that lay in ambush for the clerics. And it is a lorica of faith for the protection of body and soul against demons and men and vices: when any person shall recite it daily with pious mediation on God, demons shall not dare to face him, it shall be a protection against all poison and envy, it shall be a guard to him against sudden death, it shall be a lorica for his soul after his decease.

I include this ancient prayer in both the old Irish and English. GT recited it with unforgettable beauty. It was obviously profoundly important to him. Somehow, I know he would want it in this book. Don't ask how me how I know—I just do. And, as I told you before, this is GT's book, really, not mine.

> Atomriug indiu
> niurt tréun:
> togairm Trindóit
> cretim Treodatad
> faístin Oendatad,
> i nDúlemon dáil.
>
> Atomriug indiu
> niurt gene Críst cona bathius,
> niurt a chrochtho cona adnacul,
> niurt a essérgi cona fhresgabáil,
> niurt a thoíniudo fri brithemnas mbrátho.
>
> Atomriug indiu
> niurt gráid hiruphin,
> i n-aurlataid aingel,
> i frestul inna n-archaingel,
> i freiscisin esséirgi
> ar chiunn fochraicce,
> i n-ernaigthib uasalathrach,
> i tairchetlaib fáithe,
> i preceptaib apstal,
> i n-iresaib foísmedach,
> i n-enccai noebingen,
> i ngnímaib fer firén.

Atomriug indiu
niurt nime,
soilsi gréne,
étrochtai éscai,
áni thened,
déni lóchet,
luaithi gaíthe,
fudomnai mara,
tairismigi thalman,
cobsaidi ailech.

Atomriug indiu
niurt Dé dom luamairecht.

Cumachtae nDé dom chumgabáil,
ciall Dé dom inthús,
rose nDé dom remcisiu,
cluas Dé dom étsecht,
briathar Dé dom erlabrai,
lám Dé dom imdegail,
intech Dé dom remthechtas,
sciath Dé dom imdítin,
sochraite Dé dom anacul
ar intledaib demnae,
ar aslagib dualche,
ar forimthechtaib aicnid,
ar forimthechtaib aicnid,
ar cech duine mídúthrastar dam,
i céin ocus i n-ocus,
i núathud ocus i sochaidi.

Tocuiriur etrum indiu inna uili nert-so
fri cech nert n-amnas n-étrocar frista-i dom churp
ocus dom anmain,
fri tinchetla sa-ibfh-aithe,
fri dubrechtu gentliuchtae,
fri saíbrechtu heretecdae,
fri imchellacht n-ídlachtae,
fri brichtu ban ocus goban ocus druad,
fri cech fiss arachuille corp ocus anmain duini.

Críst dom imdegail indiu
ar neim, ar loscud, ar bádud, ar guin,
condom-thair ilar fochraicce.
Críst limm, Críst reum, Críst im degaid,
Críst indium, Críst ísum, Críst uasum,
Críst desum, Críst tuathum,
Críst i llius, Críst i sius, Críst i n-erus,
Críst i cridiu cech duini immumrorda,
Críst i ngin cech oín rodom-labrathar,
Críst i cech rusc nonom-dercathar,
Críst i cech cluais rodom-chloathar.

Atomriug indiu
niurt tréun:
togairm Trindóit,
cretim Treodatad,
faístin Oendatad,
i nDúlemon dáil.

*Domini est salus, Domini est salus, Christi est salus. Salus tua,*
*Domine, sit semper nobiscum.*[1]


I arise today
Through a mighty strength, the invocation of the Trinity,
Through the belief in the threeness,
Through confession of the oneness
Of the Creator of Creation.

I arise today
Through the strength of Christ's birth with his baptism,
Through the strength of his crucifixion with his burial,
Through the strength of his resurrection with his ascension,
Through the strength of his descent for the judgment of
    doom.

I arise today
Through the strength of the love of cherubim,
In obedience of angels,
In the service of archangels,

---

[1] The closing lines of *The Deer's Cry* are in Latin, not Gaelic.

In hope of resurrection to meet with reward,
In prayers of patriarchs,
In predictions of prophets,
In preaching of apostles,
In faith of confessors,
In innocence of holy virgins,
In deeds of righteous men.

I arise today
Through the strength of heaven:
Light of sun,
Radiance of moon,
Splendour of fire,
Speed of lightning,
Swiftness of wind,
Depth of sea,
Stability of earth,
Firmness of rock.

I arise today
Through God's strength to pilot me:
God's might to uphold me,
God's wisdom to guide me,
God's eye to look before me,
God's ear to hear me,
God's word to speak for me,
God's hand to guard me,
God's way to lie before me,
God's shield to protect me,
God's host to save me
From snares of devils,
From temptations of vices,
From everyone who shall wish me ill,
Afar and a near,
Alone and in multitude.

I summon today all these powers between me and those
    evils,
Against every cruel merciless power that may oppose my
    body and soul,
Against incantations of false prophets,

Against black laws of pagandom,
Against false laws of heretics,
Against craft of idolatry,
Against spells of witches and smiths and wizards,
Against every knowledge that corrupts man's body and
    soul.
Christ to shield me today
Against poison, against burning,
Against drowning, against wounding,
So that there may come to me abundance of reward.
Christ with me, Christ before me, Christ behind me,
Christ in me, Christ beneath me, Christ above me,
Christ on my right, Christ on my left,
Christ when I lie down, Christ when I sit down, Christ
    when I arise,
Christ in the heart of every man who thinks of me,
Christ in the mouth of everyone who speaks of me,
Christ in every eye that sees me,
Christ in every ear that hears me.

I arise today
Through a mighty strength, the invocation of the Trinity,
Through belief in the threeness,
Through confession of the oneness,
Of the Creator of Creation.

*Salvation is of the Lord, salvation is of the Lord, salvation is of
Christ. May Thy salvation, Lord, be always with us.*

# XI

## The Wasteland

"THE operation is complete," GT announced, sprinkling Holy Water liberally around the room. It had taken twenty-five minutes. "The breach has been successfully sealed. You can rest easy, now."

"Er, thanks," I said. An hour ago, I might have asked which asylum he'd escaped from. But I felt different now. Perhaps it was because—strangely—GT had truly moved me. There was something unforgettably haunting about that big man praying his prayers. All my inner protests quieted somehow. I was softening to the old geezer again.

I looked at the clock. Weird ideas were flowing through my head. I found myself pondering a variation on the cuckoo clock. Instead of a bird, though, different Piuses would pop out on the hour, proclaiming *Gloria in excelsis Deo*. Maybe they could even sing Gregorian chant. Then, I had to shake myself—hard. Whatever was I thinking?! I seemed to be going cuckoo myself. GT and his "field" were obviously getting to me.

"I believe I was talking about the Wasteland. Do you mind if we resume at that point?" GT asked. I didn't refuse him.

GT: Clearly, you care about the Wasteland, too, my friend. Your compassion for the developing world, for the environment is deeply moving.

GPL: Well, thanks, GT. I'm glad you take those things seriously, too.

GT: Any person with a heart does. Because you're absolutely right about ecological degradation. That can't continue like this. You're also right about the neoliberal economics that perpetuates a wealthy superclass, whilst countless souls live in poverty. And not just in the developing world. Have you visited any of America's rustbelt cities lately?

GPL: No. But I hear it's bad. Capitalism has been allowed to run riot in America.

GT: Yes, the propaganda for economic liberalism is incredible over there. The same propaganda tells people Catholicism is bad. The two go hand-in-hand. The Church is firmly against capitalism run riot. So it's necessary to discredit it. Meanwhile, poor people live in growing anxiety for their health and welfare—while basic necessities like medicine are controlled by business. Anxiety, such terrible non-stop anxiety…

GPL: Well, you know what I think of capitalism. But I'm glad to hear I'm not alone.

GT: No, you're not. And I think you'll find your Anna's with you there, too. Still, the Wasteland doesn't end there, for people like Anna and me. Modern capitalism, ecological catastrophe—as terrible as these things are—they're just symptoms of a deeper illness.

GPL: I know, for you, it's all down to the loss of tradition.

GT: Usury was once against Christian tradition, you know. That's partly why capitalism didn't originate in Catholic countries.

I said nothing for a moment and neither did GT. Inside, I was torn. Obviously, I didn't blame eroding tradition for the world's problems. Still, much he said was cogent. What made it more compelling was the *way* he said it. There was nothing bitter, nothing ranting in his tone of voice. GT was no angry fanatic. Instead, at times, he seemed to speak with almost infinite pain. And not for his own lot in life, but that of humanity. Once more, I suddenly couldn't help but feel sorry for the old guy. I tried to mumble something supportive.

GT: I've been watching all this for a long, long time. Longer than you think, maybe. The ever-increasing murder and suicide rates in de-traditionalised Ireland, for example. Or drugs, prostitution, domestic violence, homelessness…

These things would have shocked previous generations. But we accept them as "normal" now. And it's not stopping—but growing. Yet no-one seems to be asking: *where is all this headed in the future?*

You see, my friend, I'm not just looking at today. We need to consider the longer-term view: the world of 2100 or 2200, for example. Frankly, it scares me.

GPL: You and me, too.

GT: But there's more. The growth curves of mental illness. And the growth curves of children taking drugs to combat mental illness...

All this is just scientifically measurable mental illness. What about other forms of illness? We see this explosion of sexual perversity, sadomasochism for example. It's pathological. But you're no longer allowed to say that, of course.

In the past, these things were seen as sicknesses of the soul. Now they're normalised and accepted as an "alternative lifestyle"! It's politically incorrect to call them "sick." Soon it may be illegal to do so—what with legislation against "hate crimes" and the like.

Meanwhile, no-one ever accuses Dorkins of "hate crimes"! People like him don't sin against the prevailing orthodoxy: the New Secular Religion. They actively support it.

Let me say it again: *Secularism gets away with murder.*

GPL: Double standards are everywhere. There's no denying that.

GT: This particular one is very, very dangerous. We may be nearing the end of religious liberty. The secular metaphysic, the secular ethic, the secular elite—that small sliver of humanity—may soon have total power to crush Christian ethics. Again, the only reason secularism gets away with this is by pretending not to have a metaphysic, not to have a faith...

Moreover, the power of technology is boosting the secular metaphysic like never before. Never before has humanity been bombarded like this—round the clock. Television. Advertising. Pop songs. Jingles. Internet. iPods. And it's going to get worse. Virtual reality is coming, no doubt virtual pornography... Challenges like never before...

There's also "reproductive technology," so-called. In England, they're splicing together DNA so that a child has genes from three parents. Why not four? Why not sixteen? Where is this headed?

A child isn't a child anymore—a miracle of God. It's becoming *a product*, manipulated by technology. We're all turning into machines in a world of technocracy. Everything's becoming like steel. Steely efficiency. Steely ruthlessness. Steely cold.

Something about the way he said *steel, steely* sliced into my heart. I wasn't sure what to say. "I won't say you're right," I said at last. "But you're not wrong either. Maybe I've been too focussed on capitalism, the environment, but..." My voice trailed off.

"We all have to focus on something," GT said. "What you've done is good. I think you ought to take Anna to Africa; show her. While you're at it, take her to the Bronx, too. It's necessary to understand all these things are interrelated. The intensification of neoliberal economics—Thatcherism, Reaganism, all that—is contingent on the general coarsening of moral sensitivity. There's no solution for humanity without moral sensitivity."

And with that, he buried his head in his hands and started weeping softly again. "2100," he said a couple of times. Then, "Steel, steel..." After that, we both fell silent.

# XII

# The Hope

THERE was something terribly poignant, watching this remarkable old man weep. Again, I couldn't help but feel sorry for him.

"It can't be this bad," I said sympathetically. "You sound like you have no hope."

"There is always hope," he replied. "Indeed, I have great hope in the long term. It's the short term that concerns me: all the people, all the children, suffering in the meantime..."

Staring into the fire, GT spoke slowly. "The Church will recover," he said. "She always does. That's why She's kept going for two thousand years, when all the empires of the world caved in. The Church almost collapsed to Arianism in the fourth century. But She endured. Then came the Dark Ages. Ireland, this little island, preserved the faith, whilst pagan barbarians overran Europe. Ireland re-evangelised Europe and the Church rebounded—stronger than before. Then, came the Reformation. Catholics were persecuted in this country. For a while, the Mass was almost wiped out across northern Europe. But the Church recovered once more. It will happen again. It may take two hundred years or more. Or it may be sooner. But the Church will recover. There is my hope."

"So the only answer for humanity is the Catholic Church?" I sneered.

"I don't think Western Civilisation can survive without Christianity, no. Without it, everything becomes cold as steel." Once again, the way he said that last word was unnerving.

> GT: The only hope is the Church Christ gave us. True, the Church of Christ is most fully present in Catholicism. But it's present to nearly the same extent in the Orthodox

churches: Greek, Russian, Ukrainian, and so forth. It also functions—albeit imperfectly—through the Protestant confessions. Anyone baptised a Protestant is linked to the Church. Indeed, one cannot exclude the mysterious effects of the Holy Church, wherever people sincerely dedicate themselves to higher things.

GPL: It all sounds so simple, GT. Too simple. If only we return to Christianity, all our problems will be solved. It will be the end of nihilism, capitalism, decadence, social breakdown, murder, suicide, even climate change. Everything will be hunky-dory. I'm sorry, even if I were a Catholic, I couldn't buy that.

GT: Of course, I am not saying any such thing. The Church will never be perfect in this world. They have a very good saying in France: "The saints sin three times a day." Everyone else—obviously Catholics very much included—sins constantly.

Let's say you had a 100 percent Catholic country, filled with saints, only saints. Every member of the population would still be sinning thrice daily. Obviously, there'd still be plenty wrong with that society. Plenty. And that's a utopian, best-case scenario—completely unattainable. In reality, any Catholic society is much worse than that. You can't build heaven on earth. Even the best of us are too broken, weak, wretched...

GPL: Catholic societies are hopelessly perverse and fallen, just like everyone and everything else, then.

GT: Well, not hopelessly—but perverse and fallen, certainly.

GPL: That's a pretty dark vision you have.

GT: I am a Christian. I accept the Fall. I don't try to deny human perversity, wherever it manifests itself. Whether inside the Church or out. Of course, I don't claim there's no difference between Catholic societies and our modern materialistic wasteland!

GPL: I never expected you would!

GT: That would be almost blasphemy.

GPL: Blasphemy?!

GT: Perhaps it would be better to say: supreme faithlessness. It's tantamount to saying Christ in His Church makes no difference at all. Obviously, I don't believe that. Societies that possess the Church: Roman Catholic, Byzantine Catholic, Greek Orthodox—what have you—remain notably different from societies without the Church, without the Sacraments. Clearly, I advocate Sacramental societies over non-Sacramental societies. If you study traditional Catholic cultures, capitalism does not develop so strongly. Likewise, you don't see the same hyper-individualism, atomisation of society, breakdown of the family, social decay...

Unfortunately, today's Church doesn't understand the power of its own Sacraments. Or sacramentals—like this Holy Water or the Rosary. This is the tragedy of the post-Vatican II Church. Large parts of it have surrendered to faith in rationalism, rather than keeping faith in tradition.

The Church must recover her tradition. Only tradition understands the immense, healing power of the Sacraments. *That power can save civilisation.* If people returned to Confession, if people took the Mass seriously again, there's no telling what would happen.

But how can ordinary people take those things seriously, when the priests and bishops don't either?

Once again, he stared at the floor in terrible sadness. Then he added: "That's why Anna goes to the Latin Mass. You must understand—for her it's very, very serious. The Church has *no hope of recovery without true, reverent liturgy.* Benedict XVI said something once, when he was still Cardinal Ratzinger. What was it now...?" His voice trailed off.

"Ah, yes, I remember," GT said, suddenly speaking with great force: "'*The ecclesial crisis in which we find ourselves today depends in great part upon the collapse of the liturgy.*' Yes, Benedict XVI realised the true scope of the disaster. In her own way, so does Anna."

GPL: I see. At least, I see that's what Anna thinks...

GT: I can't expect you to understand the power of the Sacraments, GPL. You've never experienced them! For Anna and myself, it's different. We feel their potency working within us, changing us—day in, day out— transforming our souls. Bringing us into ever greater union with Him.

I've tried to tell you a little about the Church. But, of course, only a limited amount is possible in the course of a day. Why, I hardly mentioned the Resurrection!

But the Church has been given the power to resurrect. Resurrection applies not only to individuals, but also society. The Sacramental Church has the power to resurrect society, but it must claim it once more. That's why Benedict XVI—against considerable opposition—was working to restore the liturgy.

Things can't continue like this. The world can only stand so much ruthless capitalism or mental illness. Even the environment now rebels against our de-sacralising the world.

The Church will recover, like I say. Even if it takes decades. There are already signs of recovery in Russia. Eastern Orthodoxy, of course, never suffered the negative aspects of Vatican II, though it's had plenty of problems of its own...

Whatever the case, I know the power of the Sacraments. When things get bad enough, people will return to them. It's the only place where real hope lies.

GPL: Well, I can't comment on that. Like you say, I've never experienced what you're talking about.

GT: Indeed. Try to be open, GPL. Try to be open to the possibility, at least, that your Anna experiences something subtle, yet tremendous, every time she hears Mass. That's why she goes each day—even when the liturgy is dreadful. The power of the Sacrament is still at work. Anna can feel that.

Just try being open to possibilities you haven't considered, things you haven't experienced.

GPL: I'll try.

GT: Good. I think you're going to make it, you and Anna. But our time is coming to a close. It's been a delight meeting you, Mr Luxworthy, after all these years. Your name suits you admirably.

There it was again, the odd reference to the past. But, as before, I said nothing.

"Be sure to give the future Mrs Luxworthy my regards," GT said, rising from his chair. Suddenly, I felt a strange sorrow, as I too rose, seeing our session was over. I realised I might not see him for a long time—and the thought frightened me. The big, black cat nuzzled up against my leg and meowed, as if he too were saying goodbye.

"I have much to do," GT continued. "As you know, I'm off to Madrid tomorrow. And there are other situations where I'm needed. Buenos Aires, Rome. I don't get to England much. But I always return to Ireland. It's my final resting place, you might say. Perhaps we'll meet here again, one day."

Then he added, "The world is in a bad way. But I have confidence in you to make a difference. Your Anna, too, is a remarkable woman. She'll make a good wife and mother. Don't forget what I said about the Bronx. Maybe you'd like to take your honeymoon there. I can't say it's romantic—but it should rend your heart open. That's what's important: the human heart penetrated by His Heart. *Cor Jesu, Rex et Centrum omnium cordium.*"[1]

"Really, I don't know how to thank you enough," I said to him.

"No need, no need," he said. "You can write me. Here's my business card. I always read everything I receive."

I took the card and stuck it straight in my pocket, without looking. Then, his massive arms clasped me in a great big bear hug and he whispered in my ear: "*Dominus vobiscum.*" We took our leave. I closed the heavy oak door behind me and slowly descended that strange, winding staircase.

---

[1] Heart of Jesus, King and Centre of all hearts (from the *Litany of the Sacred Heart*).

# XIII

## Enchanted Evening

PARTING from GT was sad, but I felt strangely filled with hope. Obviously, he had faith that Anna and I would make it. And, despite everything, I couldn't help but have faith in GT.

At the bottom of the stairs, I looked out. It was almost twilight. A thick blanket of snow covered the street. I heard the crunch of footsteps. There coming towards me, tramping through the snow, was Anna. She apologised again for this morning. I apologised to her.

Anna hadn't even seen the priest. Before she could see him, something had happened in Dublin, she said. She'd visited a church there she liked to pray in. It was called Whitefriars and was said to hold the remains of St. Valentine, a Catholic martyr. Apparently, Pope Gregory XVI had bestowed them upon Ireland in 1836. Anna was praying by the relics of the saint, she said, when something unexpected occurred.

Whatever happened, it caused her to leave Whitefriars church immediately and drive straight back. But there was no time to talk now. She'd tell me later at the farmhouse. Right now, she was late for Mass.

The bells were ringing from Monaghan Cathedral. I walked with her as she hurried towards it. It was a majestic neo-Gothic building on a hill, although Anna lamented that, following Vatican II, the sanctuary had been garishly transformed into a gruesome monstrosity, staggeringly and hideously incongruent with the original glory and splendour.

When we reached the Cathedral, I said I'd like to come inside with her. Anna smiled at me, surprised. It would be my first ever Roman Catholic Mass. I knew I couldn't partake of the bread or wine, but Anna said I could still receive a blessing. If I folded my hands over my chest, the priest wouldn't give me the consecrated host, but bless me instead. I said I'd like that. That made her smile even more. She took my hand as we walked up the steps to the Cathedral. On entering, she dipped her hand in Holy Water and made the sign of the cross on my forehead.

We sat down at the front of the Cathedral. Anna was right about the travesty there. It was like some UFO had flown in, randomly dropping weird alien objects around, which were completely at odds with the soaring gothic windows and arches. Mechanically, I tried to copy what Anna was doing in the Mass— all that kneeling and standing. But really, I hardly noticed what was going on. My mind was awhirl with everything that had happened: GT, those extraordinary visitors, that ruby ring of fire. And what had happened to Anna in the St. Valentine's church? I couldn't wait to hear.

Before I knew it, it was time for Communion. Awkwardly, I crossed my arms like Anna told me. The bishop placed his hand over my head. His voice boomed out, "I bless you in the name of the Father and the Son and the Holy Spirit."

I was startled. Not only was I unprepared for the resounding voice, but I felt something else. I can't explain it. But something—a subtle presence of some kind—shot through me. Bewildered, I returned to my pew.

After the Mass, I insisted Anna return with me to the high street. I felt a sudden, desperate longing to see GT one last time and introduce him to Anna. Of course, I realised he might have gone by now. It was getting late. But you never know. And he said he was off to Madrid tomorrow. All the more reason to catch him tonight, before he left. Anyway, even if he weren't there, there was still that crazy sign of his. I could at least show Anna that.

That's when my world started turning inside out.

When we reached the high street, the sign was nowhere to be seen. Not only that, but there was no door either! The same barbershop and the same bookshop were still there all right. But they now stood side-by-side. The door between them, leading to that odd winding staircase, had completely vanished.

I couldn't believe my eyes. Frantically, I searched up and down the road, for any sign of that sign. Had I misremembered somehow? Maybe the sign and staircase were somewhere else. But I saw nothing, absolutely nothing.

Suddenly, I felt nauseated. "Anna, I'm not well," I said. "I had an accident in the car this morning. I hit my head. I had a concussion, I think. It must have been worse than I thought. I think you better take me to the hospital."

She looked me straight in the eye and spoke firmly. "We're going home. I have something to tell you. If you're still feeling bad after that, I'll drive you to the hospital."

Dumbly, I obeyed, getting into her car. We drove home in silence. I felt frightened. Really frightened. I couldn't have imagined the whole thing, could I? Was I losing my mind? Nothing made sense. But GT was real. Of that one thing I was absolutely sure. Perhaps parts of my experience were a hallucination. But that didn't mean the whole thing was unreal, did it? Maybe the sign, the door and the stairway were results of my concussion. Maybe GT and I had met somewhere else in town. Maybe there was no Counter-Revolutionary Carlist officer or Bee Nice or "trans-temporal from Transylvania." But GT was real—that much I knew.

When we got home, I started babbling about GT, how he seemed to know things from my past. Like what books I'd read at King's. This old man, Anna asked me, what did he look like? And did he wear a ring?

Yes, I told her, like a giant ruby glowing with celestial fire.

"What finger was it on?"

I told her it was the middle finger—not the ring finger like you'd expect.

For the longest time, Anna said nothing, absolutely nothing. She shook herself. "I have to tell you what happened in Dublin," she said at last. "I was praying at the Whitefriars Church. Suddenly, I was aware of a man standing behind me, very close. He frightened me. I knew I'd seen him before somewhere. I asked him what he wanted. He looked at me intensely and then he said something…"

Anna faltered. "What was it, Anna? What did he say?"

Slowly, as if in a dream, Anna recited his words back to me: "I have come to tell you something. You have no future as a nun. Your true vocation is caring for his soul and your children's souls."

"That's all he said: three sentences," Anna continued. "But I knew immediately he meant you. But that's not all. He took my hand and put something in my palm." She pulled it out from her handbag. It was a little yellow crocus.

"I wonder where he got that from—at this time of year?" was all I could say.

Suddenly, Anna jerked. Like something hit her. "Did you say that old man knew things about you, from King's?"

"Yes, but…"

"I knew I'd seen him before! He was the gardener there! Don't you remember? We would lie together under those trees on the Backs, reading novels."

"Howard's End," I said dumbly, as I began to remember. Anna always did have a better memory than I. Certainly, she paid better attention to people than I did.

"Yes. Exactly. He used to ask us what we were reading!"

"Anna, you're lumping too many things together. It's true, my man here in Monaghan did look a little like that old gardener. I remember now. Yes, just possibly, it's the same man. But obviously that's different from your man in Dublin."

"No, Geoffrey, you're not understanding. Your thinking's still too limited!"

"Uh, oh," I thought. "My thinking's too limited. Here we go again." In the past, comments like this were usually followed by something else. Like my head chakras not being properly aligned to the incoming Seventh Ray. What would it be this time?

"Don't you see? My man looked exactly like the man you described. He even wore the same giant ruby—on his middle finger!"

"Anna. You can't be saying it was the same man! For Pete's sake, my man was up here in Monaghan. He couldn't have been in Dublin at the same time!"

"Have you ever heard of bi-location?" she asked me.

No, I hadn't. But whatever it was, I didn't like the sound of it.

"According to tradition, certain saints are given the grace to be in two different locations at the same time. St. Padre Pio was said to bi-locate. There are reports—in the twentieth century—where people saw him in two different places at once!"

I groaned inside. I wanted to scream at Anna. Please, is there never any end to this nuttiness?! But I bit my tongue...hard.

"This man," Anna said, "Did he tell you his name?"

"Well, he said his name was Tracey, Gilbert Tracey. But then this mad Spaniard came in and started calling him Señor Valentino!"

"Valentino?" And with that Anna got up from the table and left the room. She returned with a hefty old tome, *The Irish Encyclopedia of Catholic Saints*. She thumbed to the back and started reading.

Her face went white, dead white.

"What is it, Anna. What on earth is it?"

Silently, she pushed the encyclopedia towards me. It was open to an entry for St. Valentine—a Catholic priest and exorcist, martyred in Rome on February 14, AD 269. Just before his death in prison, he wrote a letter to a blind girl called Julia. After his execution, the Roman authorities delivered the letter. According to the legend, the letter was signed "from your Valentine." And Julia's sight was restored when she opened it and found something inside—a little yellow crocus. It was his first posthumous miracle. But, as with the entire communion of saints, the book said, he still performs miracles today.

This was too much to handle. What was happening to my mind? Did I have brain damage? Signs and entire staircases that were there in the morning and gone in the evening! Bi-locating Roman saints who died 1700 years ago and consumed Irish fish and chips today! And drank root beer! And maybe committed three sins a day, for all I knew.

Then, I remembered the business card I'd stuffed in my pocket, not even looking at it. I pulled it out. There, next to an image of the Sacred Heart of Jesus, was a little yellow crocus. Underneath, it said:

---

## Gilbert Tracey

### Specialist in
### GENTLE TRADITIONALISM
#### (A Work in Progress)

Valentine@saintsabove.hvn

---

But there was no address or phone number, only an e-mail. It read: Valentine@saintsabove.hvn

"What's .hvn?" I wondered aloud, not recognizing the suffix.

"Why, it's heaven, of course, you silly," Anna beamed.

My head, which hadn't hurt since I ate that heavenly fish, started to throb with a vengeance. It was the concussion, the blasted concussion, I told myself. But it couldn't be the concussion. There was this crazy business card! Or maybe there wasn't. Maybe I was still unconscious, dreaming...

"Anna, this is insane—really, truly insane. You need to get me to that hospital," I insisted. "I've got to have my head examined. And maybe you should, too."

I'd just insulted Anna again. But she didn't seem to mind. She just smiled tenderly. In fact, she was radiant. Really, she looked so beautiful, like an angel. As though light were pouring out of her. Or maybe it was the concussion. Or the fish... maybe he'd slipped me acid in that divinely-tasting fish or something.

"It was St. Valentine in that church. I'm sure of it. It all fits together. It's his feast today! And it's our day, too. It's his sign— the crocus." Then she said slowly, "When he first told me my vocation was looking after you and our children, I didn't believe it. So I asked God for a sign if it was true. Then when I met you in town and you came to Mass with me, I knew that was it—a sign from God."

"So, you'll marry me?" was all I could say, totally dazed.

"Apparently," she said, with that Mona Lisa smile of hers.

Then, a big, beautiful smile burst out all over her face. She pulled me toward her and started kissing me. It was like that first Valentine's Day—all those years ago. (Needless to say, I forgot about the hospital instantly.)

And, as we sank into each other's arms, I could almost believe Señor Valentino was looking down on us and smiling. Perhaps he had done so from the start, in those far away gardens at King's College, Cambridge.

# XIV

## Choosing My Religion

ALL that was ten months ago. I did go to the hospital in the end. They ran tests on my head. They also looked for drugs in my system. There was nothing. I have no rational explanation for what happened. Or didn't happen. If I'm honest, I'm trying—*hard*—not to think about it.

Anyway, I'm too blissed-out to care: Anna and I are getting married in the spring.

Still, you probably wonder what I make of all this religion now. It's been tough. Certain things GT said unsettled me. Particularly, his argument that our culture has dumped the entire religious thinking of the human race—not just Christianity—whenever it didn't fit our modern ideas. That hit me like a ton of bricks. Christ, Buddha, Mohammed, Moses, Gandhi, not to mention philosophers going back to Plato and Aristotle: *wrong every time* they disagree with post-'60s liberal thinking.

I think GT was right about something else, too. We all have a religion, whether we realise it consciously or not. I used to like that old song by REM: "Losing My Religion." However, after talking to GT, I no longer think that's possible. Nobody ever loses religion—they only change it. Everybody has a creed. The trick is to choose our beliefs consciously—rather than let them choose us.

So, which religion do I choose? There appear to be plenty of choices. Somehow, though, I can't see myself converting to Buddhism or becoming a Rastafarian. I've always culturally identified with Western, European things. And, right now, I see three main choices in the West.

First, there's secularism. I've concluded GT's right. It *does* look like a covert religious system. There are too many "thou shalts" and "thou shalt nots" that people don't own up to. If you don't comply with the "politically correct" dogmas, the system labels you a heretic. At least, ordinary religion isn't covert like that. It's *upfront* about its doctrines. That way you can accept them consciously or reject them.

I never liked the capitalist media, but I didn't appreciate how downright *sneaky* it is regarding religion. GT opened my eyes here. We're all being hustled along a highway of mindless "groupthink." Atheists *are* celebrated by the media these days and, yes, it's true—traditional religion *is* pilloried. I used to think religion was limited and prejudiced. Now, I'm uncomfortably aware I never really enquired for myself. I was just parroting the "groupthink." Like GT said, secularism gets away with murder.

So where do I turn? The obvious alternative is the New Age which is everywhere you look these days. All this upbeat, positive thinking—minus critical thinking. You know what I think about that! Still, I understand the appeal of "minimum commitment spirituality." New Agers don't sign up for an official creed or set of beliefs. They think they're being less divisive, more inclusive that way. But New Agers like No Name or Bee Nice don't appear any more inclusive to me than the rest of us. If you don't fit in with their thinking, you get excluded too.

So I say "no" to crypto-religions. Instead, I start to see the value of "maximum commitment spirituality." Consciously dedicating myself to something clear and firm. It's scary as hell—but more real.

That leads me to the Church. I'm not Catholic—yet. But I'm preparing for Confirmation. So, I'm on my way. Still, it's not easy. Believing in some sort of God isn't hard. It takes more to accept Christ and the Church. But I trust Jesus was not just some nutjob, even if He talked about eating His flesh or founding His Church on the Rock of Peter. It can't just be some big illusion. Those things mean something—even if precisely what they do mean remains ultimately a mystery. People have been living—and dying—for this faith for two thousand years. I can't believe humanity has just fallen—hook, line and sinker—for some humongous two millennia con-trick by the Church.

There's also Catholic teaching on sexuality. I've had to re-think a lot there. Obviously, I used to consider the Church's laws arbitrary, stupid, biased. Now, I think I wasn't sufficiently critical of the "groupthink." These laws are hardly different from what other religions taught for thousands of years. It's hard to believe our liberal culture since the '60s has everything right and everybody else—past and present—is just a bigot. I'm reading Chesterton these days and he puts it wittily:

> Tradition means giving a vote to the most obscure of all classes, our ancestors. It is the democracy of the dead. Tradition refuses to submit to the small and arrogant oligarchy of those who merely happen to be walking about. All democrats object to men being disqualified by the accident of birth; tradition objects to their being disqualified by the accident of death. Democracy tells us not to neglect a good man's opinion, even if he is our groom; tradition asks us not to neglect a good man's opinion, even if he is our father.

Still, it's a tough struggle. I explained all my doubts to a priest. He quoted Pope St. John Paul II on faith: "Be not afraid." Did I have enough faith to proceed, he asked—to commit myself, even if I still suffered doubt? I said I did and he accepted that. Anna says it will be easier for me, once I start receiving His Body and Blood. And going to Confession and receiving absolution. My faith will be strengthened. Somehow, I actually believe that's true.

I could say far more, but it would take too long. Somehow, I have this inexplicable, deep-seated sense I'm on the right track. Let's leave it at that. As for what happened in Ireland, Anna is convinced—St. Valentine bestowed a very special grace on us. I have trouble buying that—to say the least. She says I'm stubborn, resisting reality. I still think my concussion disoriented me. I remain convinced GT is real, though. That still doesn't mean the whole thing was real. Or that he bi-located and met Anna in Dublin, two hours away. It could have been someone else—one of life's strange coincidences. Maybe there's some weird fraternity of old Irish geezers who all wear that same crazy ring. Or maybe GT knew one of them in Dublin and rang him while he made us tea in the other room...? I admit that explanation is lame. But a bi-locating saint who died in AD 269...?! Give me a break!

We're getting married after my Confirmation—and moving to Ireland. We've explored the country a lot these last ten months, looking for a place to live. It's a beautiful country, with great people, uncommonly kind. Of course, I'm sure there are plenty of Irish toerags, too. We're all fallen. But Anna was right: there's something extraordinary about Ireland, an exceptional communitarian spirit. Apparently, though, it's deteriorating. The Irish tell me everyone's out for themselves now. They say it's nowhere near as friendly as it was. If that's true, Ireland must have been *monumentally* friendly in the past.

Obviously, that change has much to do with unfettered global capitalism. *Economicism* as St. John Paul II called it. It's destroying much that is precious in Irish culture, just like everywhere else.

So I'm not only agreeing with Anna now, I'm grieving with her, too. Nations, like individuals, also choose their religion. So it isn't that Ireland is losing religion—she's just choosing a different one. Except, of course, few Irish people fully realise the choice they're making. The "groupthink" blinds us all. Global media pushes a ruthless, determined agenda. According to that agenda, the old religion, Catholicism, is bad and the new religion, which supports consumer capitalism, trash culture and hedonism generally is good.

In that sense, Ireland is choosing a different lodestar to guide her culture. In the past, it was Rome, and her Gaelic Christian heritage. Now, it's more like London and Wall Street.

Enough angst for now. Ireland remains an extraordinary country with a profound Christian heritage. Serious challenges exist, but if the Irish people can tap their deep Catholic roots, renewal is possible.

As for Anna and me, we've decided to settle in Limerick and have our children. There's a daily Latin Mass there with a French order of priests. It should be perfect for Anna, and I hope to go, too.

So—a happy ending. Life's not perfect, of course. It never is. Anna and I still fight a bit. She still apologises and goes to Confession afterwards. I guess I'll be confessing these little arguments too. We're human, fallen. Sometimes it's a relief just to admit that. Anna and I aren't the perfect couple, because no two human sinners ever will be. But, really, we're happier now than we've ever been.

I don't know what else to tell you. I just thank God every day for GT and this beautiful woman who almost, but never quite, gave up on me.

# Appendix:
# GT's Bookshelf

A last note from GPL. Here's a small list of books I saw while glancing through GT's Counter-Revolutionary bookshelf. I can't remember them all, of course. But sitting by that bookcase all day, some of the titles became strangely embedded in my mind. GT would appreciate it if they were better known, I think. Here they are:

Hilaire Belloc, *Europe and the Faith.*
Hilaire Belloc, *Survivals and New Arrivals.*
Hilaire Belloc, *The Crisis of Civilization.*
Hilaire Belloc, *The Free Press.*
Hilaire Belloc, *Monarchy: A Study of Louis XIV.*

L. Brent Bozell, *Mustard Seeds: A Conservative Becomes a Catholic.*

Stratford Caldecott, *All Things Made New.*

Warren H. Carroll, *The Crisis of Christendom.*

G. K. Chesterton, *The Everlasting Man.*
G. K. Chesterton, *Irish Impressions.*
G. K. Chesterton, *Christendom in Dublin.*

Charles A. Coulombe, *The Pope's Legion.*
Charles A. Coulombe, *Puritan's Empire.*

Christopher A. Ferrara, *Liberty, The God That Failed.*

Donal Anthony Foley, *Marian Apparitions, the Bible and the Modern World.*

Graham Greene, *The Power and the Glory.*

James Kalb, *Against Inclusiveness.*

Erik von Kuehnelt-Leddihn, *Liberty or Equality*.

Mary Kenny, *Goodbye to Catholic Ireland*.

Peter Kwasniewski, *Resurgent in the Midst of Crisis: Sacred Liturgy, the Traditional Latin Mass, and Renewal in the Church*.

John P. MacCarthy, *Twenty-first Century Ireland: A View from America*.

Michael Martin, *The Submerged Reality*.

Timothy T. O'Donnell, *Heart of the Redeemer*.

Timothy T. O'Donnell, *Swords Around the Cross—The Nine Years' War: Ireland's Defense of Faith and Fatherland 1594–1603*.

Patrick Pearse, *The Coming Revolution*.

Thomas Storck, *From Christendom to Americanism and Beyond: The Long, Jagged Trail to a Postmodern Void*.

J.R.R. Tolkien, *The Return of the King*.

Valentin Tomberg, *Degeneration and Regeneration of Jurisprudence*.

Valentin Tomberg, *Foundations of International Law as Humanity's Law*.

Valentin Tomberg, *Lazarus Come Forth*.

John Waters, *Was It For This? Why Ireland Lost the Plot*.

Frederick Wilhelmsen, *Hilaire Belloc: No Alienated Man*.

34913382R00110

Made in the USA
San Bernardino, CA
09 June 2016